BONKERS BOOKS

How to make STONEHENGE out of BISCUITS

a YEAR'S worth of crazy IDEAS!

WRITTEN BY

Tracey Turner

Illustrated by **Clive Goddard**

SCHOLASTIC

Scholastic Children's Books,
Euston House, 24 Eversholt Street,
London, NW1 1DB, UK

A division of Scholastic Ltd
London ~ New York ~ Toronto ~ Sydney ~ Auckland
Mexico City ~ New Delhi ~ Hong Kong

First published in the UK by Scholastic Ltd, 2011

Text copyright © Tracey Turner, 2011
Illustration copyright © Clive Goddard, 2011
All rights reserved

ISBN 978 1407 11598 6

Printed and bound in the UK by CPI Bookmarque Ltd, Croydon, Surrey

2 4 6 8 10 9 7 5 3 1

The BRILLIANTLY bonkers book of mad activities for every day of the YEAR

NOTE

Before attempting any of the many exciting things to do in this book, beware. Remember to always...

* Make sure an adult knows where you are at all times.
* Follow safety advice and wear safety clothing where appropriate.
* Take special care when cooking or using sharp knives or scissors.
* Ask an adult to help you when using the oven or hob.

The publisher and author of this book do not accept responsibility for accident or injury that results from the information in this book.

→ INTRODUCTION

In this book you will find something interesting, surprising or even amazing about every single day of the year. It might turn an otherwise boring Monday into a day for hugging cats, or wearing a gorilla suit, for example. Or perhaps today is an ancient Roman trumpet festival, or Roald Dahl's birthday, or an Italian orange-throwing carnival. Discover which day of the year is...

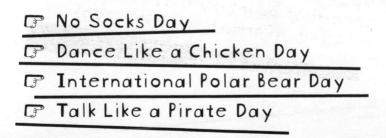

☞ No Socks Day

☞ Dance Like a Chicken Day

☞ International Polar Bear Day

☞ Talk Like a Pirate Day

Having marvelled at the day's Interesting Thing, you can find ideas or instructions for something to do for each day – though whether you decide to do it or not is up to you. Some things are definitely NOT recommended for the uninitiated, but might be exciting ideas for the future: shovel racing, water jousting and eating stinging nettles, for example. But there are lots of things you might want to try. As well as building Stonehenge out of biscuits, you can find out how to...

☞ Write a HORROR story

☞ Make a fizz-propelled ROCKET

☞ Use Morse CODE

☞ Find NORTH without a compass

No day need ever be dull again.

1 January
Samuel Pepys began his diary

On this day in 1660 Pepys began his famous diary. Why not begin your own — either in the old fashioned way with a pen and paper, or by starting a blog? Have a look at www.howtostartablog.org. You could blog about anything that interests you — from outer space to bell-ringing to guinea pigs to Dr Who.

2 January
The unluckiest day of the year

At least, that's what the Saxons used to believe. Have a duvet day to be on the safe side.

3 JANUARY

Tutankhamun's tomb discovered

Howard Carter discovered the ancient Egyptian boy king's tomb today in 1924. So...

Learn how to write your name in hieroglyphs

Ancient Egyptian scribes took years to learn how to write using this system. You're probably a bit pressed for time, so try this simplified version instead.

4 January

Women reach the South Pole

On 4 January 2000 Catherine Hartley and Fiona Thornewill were among the first women to complete a freezing trek across Antarctica to reach the South Pole, over 1,000 km. If it's snowing, why not build a snow-woman to commemorate their achievement?

BUILD A SNOW-WOMAN

• Make three giant snowballs – these will be the base, middle and head.

• Put the biggest snowball at the bottom, standing it firmly on the ground.

• Add the second biggest snowball, remembering to give your snow-woman a nice waist.

• Add the head – form an elegant neck if possible.

• Add features – a carrot is a traditional nose, but you could also use the end of a cucumber or courgette. Make lips from a red pepper. You could use biscuits for eyes and matchsticks for eyelashes.

• Dress your snow-woman. You might look out a fetching bikini, a poncho, or just the traditional scarf and hat.

5 January (early January)
Mad Maldon mud race

Every year in early January, hundreds of people get very muddy racing 400 metres across the estuary in Maldon, UK, at low tide. The runners need a tetanus jab and have to tape their shoes to their feet! If you can't make it to Maldon, go for a muddy winter walk instead.

6 January
Twelfth Night

Take down your Christmas decorations — it's supposed to be bad luck if you haven't done it by now.

7 January
Christmas Day in the Russian Orthodox Church

You thought Christmas was all over — but here's your chance to celebrate all over again!

8 January
Festival of Kings

Every year around this date (the first Sunday after 6 January), people in Paris, France, celebrate the **Fête des Rois** (Festival of Kings) with a special cake known as the **Galette des Rois** (Kings' Cake). Inside the cake's marzipan filling is a china figurine known as **la fève**. The person who gets **la fève** in their piece of cake becomes King or Queen for the day. They wear a paper crown and get to order everyone about. Make your own version of the **Galette des Rois**, using any recipe you like, and put your own **fève** into the mixture. Be warned though, you could end up being ordered about by your little brother...

9 January
The first modern circus was staged

...in 1768 in London, UK, by Philip Astley. To remember this historic event, today is the perfect day to...

LEARN HOW TO JUGGLE

1. Start by using one ball. Practise throwing it from hand to hand in an arc. Try and make it reach the same height each time (this should be about eye level).

2. Move on to two balls. Throw the ball in your right hand as you did with just one ball. When it reaches its highest point, throw the ball in your left hand. Catch the first ball with your left hand and the second ball with your right. Practise doing this starting with your left hand too.

3. Now try juggling three balls. Start with two balls in your right hand, one behind the other, and one ball in your left hand.

4. Throw the front ball in your right hand in an arc to your left hand.

5. When the first ball is at its highest point, throw the ball in your left hand over to your right hand.

6. Catch the first ball with your left hand. When the second ball is at its highest point, throw the other ball in your right hand over to your left hand.

7. Catch the second ball with your right hand.

8. Keep going!

10 JANUARY
Make wintery snowflakes
Cheer yourself up in the winter weather by making some snowflakes. This way of making them is popular in Poland, where they're known as gwiazdy (stars).

MAKE SNOWFLAKES

1. Take a square of paper and fold it in half, in half again, and then in half diagonally to make a triangle.

2. Draw a curve along the top edge and cut it, to make a cone shape.

3. Draw triangles, semi-circles and other shapes down the sides – make them the same on each side and then cut them out.

4. Open up your paper to reveal your snowflake.

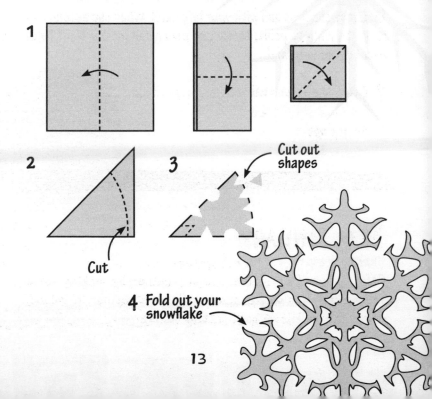

1

2

Cut

3

Cut out shapes

4 Fold out your snowflake

13

11 January (winter)
Avantouinniti

In Finland, ice holes are maintained throughout winter for the hard-as-nails people who want to take part in avantouinniti, or ice swimming. Whatever you do, don't try this at home.

12 January (mid-January)
Conconully Outhouse Races

Every January, the town of Conconully in Washington State, USA, hosts this unusual race. Outside toilets (which must include a toilet seat and toilet paper on a hanger) are mounted on skis and raced down the snow-covered main street. You could make up a team with two friends (each team must have two pushers and one rider).

13 January
The coldest day of the year

Today is supposed to be the coldest day of the year. Make sure you're nice and warm – make yourself some hot chocolate with whipped cream, chocolate flakes and marshmallows on top.

14 January
Dress Up Your Pet Day

No one seems to know how this unusual holiday first started, but every 14 January cats and dogs all over the world (and especially in the US) are dressed up in hats, jackets, jumpers and shoes. Why not take part with your own pet? Or check out some of the amazing outfits your pet could be wearing on the Internet.

15 JANUARY (mid-January)
Icebox Days Festival
Visit International Falls in Minnesota, USA, for its four-day winter festival, where you can make a snow sculpture, go skiing by candlelight or try your hand at frozen turkey bowling. Or if you can't make it to Minnesota, you could bowl with ice cubes or snowballs instead.

16 January

Appreciate a Dragon Day

This day of appreciation for fiery friends everywhere was set up by children's author Donita K Paul. Write your own dragon story, create dragon art, or read your favourite dragon tales today.

17 January

Peter Roget's

Peter Roget, author of Roget's Thesaurus (a book that lists groups of words with similar meanings), was born today in 1779. Browse through a thesaurus today and broaden your vocabulary. For example...

INSTEAD OF SAYING...	TRY...
Boring	Tedious, drab, monotonous, soporific
Walk	Stroll, saunter, stride, march, tramp
Loud	Strident, ear-splitting, explosive

18 January

A A Milne's birthday

A A Milne, author of the classic children's books about Winnie-the-Pooh, was born on 18 January 1882. Celebrate by playing Winnie-the-Pooh's favourite game...

PLAY POOH STICKS

YOU NEED: at least two people; several sticks; a small bridge over a river or stream

1. Each player should select a stick – it can be any shape or size but players must make sure they can recognize their own stick.

2. Players stand on one side of the bridge with the water running in the opposite direction.

3. On a count of three, each player must drop his or her stick over the side of the bridge.

4. Players run to the other side of the bridge.

5. The winner is the player whose stick emerges from underneath the bridge first.

19 January

Edgar Allan Poe's birthday

Today is the birthday of writer Edgar Allan Poe, born in 1809. He is famous for his mystery and horror stories. Today is the perfect day to...

WRITE YOUR OWN HORROR STORY

✻ *CHOOSE YOUR SUPER-SPOOKY SETTING. Here are some suggestions...*

A haunted house
A graveyard
A school scheduled for demolition
A deep, dark wood
A ruined castle
An abandoned warehouse

✻ *CHOOSE YOUR MAIN CHARACTER(S)*

✻ *DECIDE ON YOUR PLOT. Here are some suggestions...*

A stranger knocks at the door – it's the middle of nowhere and he's lost...

A violent thunderstorm cuts the power ... did someone – or something – creep into the house in the dark?

A ghost needs to be avenged before it stops haunting the living – you discover it's the ghost of a Victorian teacher...

✳ *CHOOSE SOME SCARY CHARACTERS. Here are some suggestions:*

ghosts
witches
zombies
vampires

✳ *MAKE SURE YOUR STORY HAS A BEGINNING, A MIDDLE AND A TERRIFYING END.*

20 January

Ice weather for it...

Whether or not the weather's icy, try this weird and wonderful ice experiment...

MAKE ICE SPIKES

1. Fill an ice-cube tray with distilled water.

2. Put it in the freezer overnight.

3. Take the ice out of the freezer. You should find that a few of the ice cubes have spikes growing out of them. This happens because the water in each section of the tray freezes from the outside in, leaving an unfrozen patch in the middle. Ice takes up more room than water, so the ice forces the remaining water up through the unfrozen patch. This then freezes, too, forming a spike. This works best with distilled water because there are small amounts of salts in tap water which stop the spikes from forming.

21 January

National Hugging Day

This extremely friendly day was founded in the US in 1986, but has now been embraced by lots of different countries around the world. If you haven't already given someone a big cuddle today, get started immediately by hugging your mum or your best friend.

22 JANUARY (21 January – 20 February)
Chinese New Year

The Chinese New Year falls some time between 21 January and 20 February. Chinese years are named after one of twelve animals, and your Chinese horoscope depends on what year you were born. Check out which animal you are below.

RAT YEARS

1924, 1936, 1948, 1960, 1972, 1984, 1996, 2008

OX YEARS

1925, 1937, 1949, 1961, 1973, 1985, 1997, 2009

TIGER YEARS

1926, 1938, 1950, 1962, 1974, 1986, 1998, 2010

RABBIT YEARS

1927, 1939, 1951, 1963, 1975, 1987, 1999, 2011

DRAGON YEARS

1928, 1940, 1952, 1964, 1976, 1988, 2000, 2012

SNAKE YEARS

1929, 1941, 1953, 1965, 1977, 1989, 2001, 2013

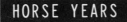

HORSE YEARS

1930, 1942, 1954, 1966, 1978, 1990, 2002, 2014

SHEEP YEARS

1931, 1943, 1955, 1967, 1979, 1991, 2003, 2015

MONKEY YEARS

1920, 1932, 1944, 1956, 1968, 1980, 1992, 2004

ROOSTER YEARS

1921, 1933, 1945, 1957, 1969, 1981, 1993, 2005

DOG YEARS

1922, 1934, 1946, 1958, 1970, 1982, 1994, 2006

PIG YEARS

1923, 1935, 1947, 1959, 1971, 1983, 1995, 2007

23 JANUARY

Anniversary of Claude Chappe's death

Claude Chappe died today in 1805. Chappe invented a system that could communicate messages over long distances. This system was called semaphore. Semaphore was very handy in the days before the Internet and text messaging. Use today to…

LEARN HOW TO SEND A SEMAPHORE MESSAGE

24 January

Boy Scout movement's anniversary

On this day in 1908, the Boy Scout movement began in the UK. Why not pitch a tent and spend the night outdoors – even if it's only in your back garden? If it's really cold you could cheat and put your tent up in the living room.

25 January

Burns' Night

This is the traditional day to celebrate the poetry of Scottish poet Robert Burns...

HOST A BURNS' SUPPER

YOU NEED: guests; soup, haggis, bagpipe player
1. Make a short speech welcoming your guests.
2. Before dinner, say the Selkirk Grace:

Some hae meat and canna eat,
And some wad eat that want it;
But we hae meat, and we can eat,
Sae let the Lord be thankit.

3. Serve the soup - Scotch broth is a good choice.
4. After the first course, bring the haggis into the room.
5. Stand up, if possible the accompaniment of someone playing the bagpipes, and recite Robert Burns' poem,

'Address to a Haggis'. Here is the first verse:

Fair fa' your honest, sonsie face,
Great chieftain o' the puddin-race!
Aboon them a' ye tak your place,
Painch, tripe, or thairm:
Weel are ye wordy o' a grace
As lang's my arm.

6. Eat the haggis.
7. Ask your guests to make their own speeches.
8. Recite (or ask your guests to recite) more Burns' poetry.

26 JANUARY

Australia Day

Australians celebrate Australia Day in different ways, and perhaps the most 'different' of all is the Cockroach Racing World Championships. You could go and watch the race at the Story Bridge Hotel in Brisbane, or you could take part – the hotel sells cockroaches if you don't have one. Failing that, stage your own creepy-crawly race with ants, woodlice, earwigs, or any obliging small creature you can find.

25

27 JANUARY

Mozart's birthday

The famous composer Wolfgang Amadeus Mozart was born today in 1756. Spend the day appreciating music – it doesn't have to be classical. You could make your all-time favourite playlist.

28 JANUARY

Gianluigi Buffon's birthday

Goalkeeper Gianluigi Buffon was born on 28 January 1978. So use today to...

PRACTISE SAVING A PENALTY KICK

• You won't have time to judge which way to dive after the penalty taker has struck the ball – make a decision beforehand and dive the instant the striker's foot touches the ball.

• Check out whether the penalty taker is looking at a particular spot in the goal mouth as they get ready. It can reveal where he or she is planning to kick the ball.

- Is the striker right- or left-footed? If the player is right-footed, the ball will most likely go to the left-hand side of the goal, and vice versa.
- As the striker approaches the ball, notice the direction of his or her hips — this is the direction the ball is likely to travel in.

- Use both hands, and fully extend your arms, as you dive.

- Remember that there is more pressure on the penalty taker than on the goalkeeper. The average number of penalty saves in the Premiership is 28 out of 100.

29 JANUARY
Anniversary of the first Victoria Cross
The Victoria Cross, the medal awarded in the UK for bravery, was first issued today in 1856. Do something brave today — perhaps you could overcome your fear of spiders, heights, snakes or speaking in public.

30 JANUARY
Anniversary of King Charles I's death
On 30 January 1649, King Charles I of England was beheaded at the Banqueting Hall in Whitehall, London. If you go to the Banqueting Hall today, you'll find that there is still a ceremony to commemorate the event on 30 January.

CIVIL WAR QUIZ

1. King Charles I's supporters were called...
a) Cantilevers
b) Caballeros
c) Cavaliers

2. How did the Roundheads (King Charles' enemies) get their name?
a) The shape of their haircuts
b) The shape of their helmets
c) The shape of their sword handles

3. Whose head turned up in a freak show labelled 'The Monster's Head' in 1710, and was finally buried in 1960?
a) Charles I
b) Charles II
c) Oliver Cromwell

4. What was King Charles II known as?
a) The Laughing Cavalier
b) The Sun King
c) The Merry Monarch

Answers: 1)c; 2)b; 3)c; 4)c.

31 JANUARY
National Gorilla Suit Day

It really is – in the US at least. It's a holiday that was created in 1964 by a cartoonist named Don Martin, and it continues to be observed around the world. So wear a gorilla suit – you know you want to.

FEBRUARY

1 FEBRUARY
Kiss a passion fruit
Superstition says that if you kiss a passion fruit on 1 February, all of your dreams will come true.

2 FEBRUARY
Groundhog Day
According to folklore, if a groundhog (an American rodent) leaves its burrow today and sees its shadow, it will retreat back into its burrow and the winter will continue for another six weeks. If it doesn't, and stays out of its burrow, it means that winter is over. Instead of a groundhog, see if your pet can predict the weather in a similar way.

3 FEBRUARY
Bean-throwing Festival

In Japan, Setsunbun-sai, the Bean-throwing Festival, marks the end of winter. Today, you should throw beans into each room of the house and then out of the outside doors, shouting, 'Devils out, fortune in!' Make sure you use dried beans, baked beans make a bit of a mess.

4 FEBRUARY (first Sunday in February)
Clowns' Service

Holy Trinity Church in Dalston, London, UK, holds its annual Clowns' Service on the first Sunday in February. It's attended by professional and amateur clowns from all over the country, dressed in full costume and make-up, to commemorate the life of the famous clown Joseph Grimaldi. Wear a squirty flower in his honour and see how many people you can trick with it.

5 FEBRUARY

The first flowers of the year

Are there any flowers in your garden yet? If not, make your own daffodils to brighten things up...

MAKE DAFFODILS

YOU NEED: crepe paper (yellow, orange and green); 20 cm length of garden wire; glue

1. Cut a rectangle of orange crepe paper about 2 x 5 cm. Stretch one of the long edges to make a frill. Roll it into a tube and twist the bottom around the garden wire. Glue it in place.

2. Cut out six petal shapes from yellow crepe paper. Stretch the edges, then glue each one to the base of the orange trumpet.

3. Wrap strips of green crepe paper around the flower base and down the wire. Secure it in place with glue.

6 FEBRUARY

Waitangi Day

6 February is a special day in New Zealand celebrating the signing of the Treaty of Waitangi in 1840 by representatives of

Britain and the Maori people. It's celebrated with festivals and public concerts, often including reggae music because today is also reggae singer Bob Marley's birthday. If you can't get to New Zealand to celebrate, at least listen to some Bob Marley songs.

7 FEBRUARY
Charles Dickens' birthday

The famous writer was born on 7 February 1812. Visit Charles Dickens' birthplace, at 393 Old Commercial Road, Portsmouth, UK. It's shut during the winter months, except for 7 February.

WRITE LIKE CHARLES DICKENS

• Choose a grand theme, such as the divide between the rich and poor, with plenty of slums, starvation, ill-health, and perhaps a prison. Make sure there's some love interest, too.

• Give your story lots of characters, and add detailed descriptions of their physical characteristics. Give them appropriate names, for example, an evil teacher who beats his pupils might be Mr Thrasher.

• Write lots. Charles Dickens' books are very long, and are divided into many chapters.

8 FEBRUARY (various dates in February)
World Shovel Racing Championships

Every February the town of Angel Fire, New Mexico, USA, hosts the World Shovel Racing Championships. Taking part is not recommended. Riders sit on a shovel with their legs in the air on either side of the handle, and go plummeting down a 300-metre hill. If you're not near New Mexico today, maybe you could go sledging. Or, if there's no snow around, try riding your bike or skateboarding instead.

9 FEBRUARY (second Monday in February)
Clean Out Your Computer Day

Clean Out Your Computer Day is sponsored by the Institute of Business Technology in the US. Today is the day to delete all the files and contacts you don't need any more, uninstall programmes you don't use, and make sure everything's backed up. Why not go bonkers and do your homework and tidy your room at the same time?

10 FEBRUARY
Queen Victoria's wedding anniversary

Queen Victoria of England was married to Prince Albert on 10 February 1840. Impress your history teacher with some...

FASCINATING QUEEN VICTORIA FACTS

• There were seven attempts to kill Queen Victoria. The first time, in 1840, she was shot at twice while travelling in her carriage. In 1871 she was attacked by a man waving a pistol and was saved when her favourite servant, John Brown, heroically leapt on the man and flattened him. Victoria wasn't injured during any of the attempts on her life.

• Victoria's husband, Prince Albert, died after they had been married for 22 years. Victoria mourned him for the rest of her long life and always dressed in black.

• Prince Arthur, Queen Victoria's son, shot out his brother-in-law Prince Christian's, eye during a shooting trip. Prince Christian kept a collection of glass eyes, which he liked to show people at dinner parties (his favourite was a bloodshot one).

11 FEBRUARY
Thomas Edison's birthday

Today is the birthday of the American inventor Thomas Edison, who was born in 1847. Thomas Edison is probably most famous for inventing the light bulb. In fact, he didn't invent it, but he did improve an earlier invention and made it into something really useful. Have a go at improving an invention today. How about making healthy sweets or a type of homework that does itself?

12 February
Darwin Day

Charles Darwin was born on 12 February 1809. Charles Darwin was one of the most famous scientists who ever lived, and was absolutely bonkers about plants and animals. He spent his life travelling around the world studying living things and publishing his findings in books.

Darwin's most famous book was called **The Origin of Species**. It made the idea of evolution popular for the first time. To celebrate the life of Darwin, why not go outside and study some of the plants and animals in your local park or back garden?

13 February
Roman festival of purification

February gets its name from the ancient Roman festival of purification called Februa, held around this date. It was the original spring-cleaning day, so have a good clean up.

14 FEBRUARY
Saint Valentine's Day

Sending a card but stuck for inspiration? Why not say it with someone else's words? Here are a few quotations to impress your loved one...

- **A life without love is like a sunless garden where all the flowers are dead. – Oscar Wilde**

- **Love makes your soul crawl out from its hiding place. – Zora Neale Hurston**

- **Nothing takes the taste out of peanut butter quite like unrequited love. – Charlie Brown**

15 FEBRUARY
Galileo Galilei's birthday

Along with lots of other amazing inventions and discoveries, Galileo came up with a brilliant new design for the telescope, which he used to discover the moons of Jupiter, the rings of Saturn (although he didn't know what they were) and lots more. Impress your friends with your amazing knowledge: learn the names of the Galilean Moons of Jupiter (they're the four biggest): Io, Europa, Ganymede and Callisto.

16 FEBRUARY

John McEnroe's birthday

The tennis commentator, and former world number one professional tennis player, John McEnroe, was born on 16 February 1959. To mark the day...

LEARN HOW TO SERVE A TENNIS BALL

1. Face the net and point your racquet in the direction you want the ball to travel.

2. With the racquet in one hand and the ball in the other, raise both your hands together in the same direction, and then bring them down together. At the same time, transfer your weight to your back foot.

3. Raise your throwing hand above your head and throw the ball upwards and slightly forwards.

4. Swing your racquet back, as if you were going to scratch your back with it, and hit the ball, transferring your weight onto your front foot.

5. The higher up you can hit the ball, the more power it will have. Keep your racquet arm straight and follow it through with your body.

6. Keep practising until you have mastered it.

17 February

Celebrate the patron saint of television

On 17 February 1958, Pope Pius XII declared Saint Clare of Assisi the patron saint of television. So, put your feet up and watch a bit of telly.

18 February

The discovery of Pluto

On this day in 1930, the planet Pluto was discovered and became the ninth planet in our solar system. Sadly for Pluto, it was demoted to a dwarf planet in 2006. Now the eight planets in the solar system (from closest to the Sun to furthest away) are:

Mercury

Venus

EARTH

Mars

Jupiter

Saturn

Uranus

Neptune

To remember them, you could make up a sentence using the first letter of each planet to start each word. Try this one:

My Very Endearing Mule Just Sat (on an) Upturned Newt

19 February
Anniversary of the phonograph

On 19 February 1878, Thomas Edison invented the phonograph, which was the forerunner of the record player, which was the forerunner of the CD player … which was the forerunner of the MP3 player. To celebrate, try making a playlist of one really good or special song taken from each year of your life.

20 February (1 February – 1 March)
Ivrea Carnevale

Lent is the Christian festival of fasting, or not eating very much. Just before it begins, the town of Ivrea in northern Italy holds its unique carnival, which commemorates a twelfth-century battle. This is your chance to become involved in a massive orange-throwing fight. The streets soon become slippery with squashed fruit. If you don't want to be pelted by oranges, you have to buy a special red hat.

21 February (between 3 February and 9 March)
Shrove Tuesday

Shrove Tuesday is the last day before Lent. It is traditional for Christians to prepare for the day by using up the food in their cupboards and making pancakes.

LEARN HOW TO FLIP A PANCAKE

1. Make some pancake mixture and fry it in a pan for about a minute. Check the underneath is cooked by shaking the pan: if the pancake slides about easily, it's done.

2. Take the frying pan off the stove and tilt it away from you, then pull the pan back towards you and up at the same time, with a small flick.

3. The pancake should flip over onto its uncooked side – watch carefully and be ready with the frying pan so that the pancake lands flat.

4. If you've never tried this before, the chances are that the pancake will land in a twisted mess in the frying pan, or on the floor. You need to keep practising to perfect the art of pancake flipping.

5. Once you've become skilled, invite your friends over for a demonstration and a feast.

22 FEBRUARY
Robert Baden-Powell's birthday

Robert Baden-Powell, founder of the Scout movement, was born today in 1857. Wear a woggle today, or take part in a scouting activity such as canoeing, camping or rock climbing.

23 FEBRUARY
Feast Day of Saint Serenus the Gardener

Catholic Saint Serenus was famous for his beautiful garden. Do some gardening to prepare for spring and...

Plant Nasturtium Seeds

Nasturtiums have beautiful, bright flowers and are easy to grow. You can plant them straight outside into the soil or into pots at this time of year. Choose a sunny spot. If you're sowing into the ground, give the soil a good rake first. Make holes about 2 cm deep and 2 cm apart, and pop the seeds in holes. Cover them with soil and water well.

24 FEBRUARY

Flag Day in Mexico

Today is a national holiday in Mexico – **La Dia de la Bandera**, the day of the flag. Throw a Mexican party and include a special Mexican tradition...

MAKE A CHEAT'S PIÑATA

YOU NEED: Large, sturdy paper bag (with a square bottom); felt pens or paints; coloured tissue paper; glue or tape; scissors; string; small sweets

1. Colour the paper bag in a bold, bright design with your pens or paints.

2. Cut the tissue paper into fringes and attach them to the bag – make four or five fringes for each side of the bag.

3. Half fill the bag with sweets and other goodies.

4. Fold down the top and secure it with tape or glue.

5. Punch two holes in the top of your piñata, thread it with string and hang it up.

7. Take it in turns to pop on a blindfold and whack it with a rolled-up newspaper until the sweets are released.

25 February

Pierre-Auguste Renoir's birthday

Impressionist artist Pierre-Auguste Renoir was born today in 1841. To celebrate, you could...

PAINT YOUR OWN IMPRESSIONIST PAINTING

1. Most Impressionists liked to paint outdoors. So, put on your coat, and perhaps a beret, and set up your art stuff somewhere picturesque.

2. Choose a natural scene and paint quickly. Don't worry about being too realistic, it's the overall 'impression' that's important, not the details.

3. Don't blend your colours — paint red next to yellow to create an illusion of orange. Avoid using black paint and strong outlines.

4. Use short brush strokes and paint in thick dollops.

5. When you have finished, stand a distance away from your easel to admire your masterpiece.

26 FEBRUARY

National Chilli Day

Today is National Chilli Day in the US. So ...

MAKE CHILLI CON CARNE

YOU NEED: olive oil; 1 medium onion; 2 cloves of garlic; 1 stick of celery; 2 red peppers; 1 tsp chilli powder; 1 tsp cumin; 500 g lean minced beef; 1 x 400 g tin of chickpeas; 1 x 400 g tin of red kidney beans; 2 x 400 g tins of chopped tomatoes

1. Heat a tablespoon of olive oil in a large saucepan.

2. Chop the onion, celery and garlic and add to the pan. Fry for a couple of minutes.

3. Chop the red pepper and add to the pan. Fry for another couple of minutes.

4. Add the minced beef, the chilli powder and the cumin. Fry for 10 minutes.

5. Drain the tins of chickpeas and kidney beans and add them, along with the tins of tomatoes.

6. Turn down the heat to a simmer and cook for about an hour, stirring every so often.

7. Serve with rice or flour tortillas and guacamole.

27 FEBRUARY

International Polar Bear Day

Yes, really – once a year, on 27 February, it's your chance to celebrate polar bears. Fascinate your friends with some facts about them...

• A polar bear's fur isn't really white - it's transparent. The coarser, outer hairs are hollow, reflecting the light to make it look white.

• In zoos, polar bears have been known to turn green, because of small plants called algae, growing inside their hollow hair shafts.

• A polar bear's skin is black. Underneath, a layer of blubber up to 11.5 cm thick protects the bear from the cold.

• Polar bears are the world's biggest land predator. Male polar bears can measure three metres long and weigh more than 700 kg.

28 February

Kalevala Day

Kalevala is a Finnish epic poem, celebrated today along with all Finnish national culture. Make something Finnish today.

MAKE FINNISH TRIFLE

This delicious pudding can be thrown together quickly – in Finland it's known as 'the dessert for unexpected visitors'.

YOU NEED: 200 g biscuit crumbs; 100 ml apple juice; 200 ml jam; 200 ml whipped cream; 1 tsp sugar

1. Pour the juice over the biscuit crumbs.

2. Whip the cream with the sugar until it's light and fluffy.

3. Put a layer of crumbs, then a layer of jam, then a layer of cream into a dessert bowl and put it in the fridge for a couple of hours.

29 February

Leap day

There are only 29 days in February once every four years, during a leap year. On 29 February 2004, the film The Lord of the Rings: The Return of the King won 11 Oscars, equalling the record set by Ben Hur and Titanic.

The Return of the King was the only film to have won all categories it was nominated for. Celebrate by hosting a movie night – complete with popcorn. Dim the lights and show your friends to their seats with a torch.

MARCH

1 MARCH
Saint David's Day

Wear a leek in your hat

It's traditional to wear a leek in your hat on Saint David's Day, the feast day of the patron saint of Wales. Whether you're Welsh or not, why not have a party to celebrate? Pop a leek in your hat or pin a daffodil (the Welsh traditional flower) to your jumper and invite some friends over. You could serve lava bread, a traditional Welsh bread made from seaweed.

2 MARCH
Celebrate Your Name Week

The first week in March is Celebrate Your Name Week. Celebrate Your Name week was founded in 1997 as a day for people to appreciate their names and find out more about them. Spend today finding out about your name and whether you have any famous namesakes.

3 MARCH
Alexander Graham Bell's birthday

Alexander Graham Bell, inventor of the telephone, was born on this day in 1847. Spend the day catching up with your friends — what a brilliant excuse for a day of chatting and texting ... as if you need one.

4 MARCH
Antonio Vivaldi's birthday

The famous composer Antonio Vivaldi was born on this day in 1678. To celebrate, why not have a go at composing your own piece of music. Obviously, it helps if you are an expert in musical theory, but don't let it stop you if you're not! Use a keyboard, a guitar or even a recorder if you're desperate, and experiment.

5 MARCH

Saint Piran's Day

Today is Saint Piran's Day, feast day of the patron saint of tin miners from Cornwall, UK. To celebrate, miners were given the day off work. Celebrate it yourself and...

MAKE CORNISH PASTIES

YOU NEED: 600 g ready-made short-crust pastry; 1 x large onion; 150 g potato; 150 g swede; 450 g braising steak

1. Chop the meat, onion, potato and swede into small pieces. Divide each ingredient into four equal portions.

2. Roll out the pastry into four circles, 20 cm across and about as thick as a pound coin.

3. Layer the ingredients in the middle of each circle. Start with half a portion of potato, then add half a portion of swede, a portion of meat, and a portion of onion. Finish with the other half of the potato and swede. Season each layer with pepper and a little salt.

4. Carefully bring the edges of each pastry circle into the middle. Pinch the pastry to close it.

5. Put the pasties into a pre-heated oven at 180°C/ gas mark 4. Bake for one hour, until golden brown.

6 MARCH (February or March)

Holi

In the Hindu festival of Holi, people celebrate by throwing coloured water or powder at one another, swapping presents and generally having fun. Why not join in? Get some mates together, put on some old clothes, mix up some (washable) paints, and see who ends up the messiest. Do this outside, or be prepared to do a lot of cleaning up afterwards.

7 MARCH

Amundsen reached the South Pole

On 7 March 1912 Roald Amundsen announced that he had become the first person to reach the South Pole. Why not mount your own expedition? You don't need to go that far. Try the uncharted territories of a forest, moorland or mountain near you. Make sure you have more than one colleague in your expedition, and leave detailed notes telling everyone at base camp (home) where you are going and when you expect to be back.

SOUTH POLE

8 MARCH
International Women's Day

Who is your Women's Day heroine? Spend the day doing some research into the lives of some of the greatest women who ever lived. Here are some ideas...

HYPATIA (4th century philosopher and scientist)

HARRIET TUBMAN (organizer of the Underground Railroad)

MARY WOLLSTONECRAFT (pioneering early feminist)

ADA LOVELACE (18th century computer programmer)

MARY KINGSLEY (intrepid Victorian explorer)

AMELIA EARHART (fearless flight pioneer)

ROSA PARKS (courageous Civil Rights activist)

HELEN KELLER (deaf and blind writer, lecturer and political activist)

9 MARCH

Have a winter picnic

It's almost spring ... why not celebrate with a winter picnic?
If it's pouring with rain you could have an indoor one. But if
not, wrap up warm have it outside – it's not that cold...

• Winter picnics are best eaten after a long, bracing walk.

• If possible, use insulated backpacks to carry your picnic supplies.

• Make sure you bring one flask filled with hot chocolate, and
another for hot soup.

• Take hot sausages or pasties wrapped in tin foil and several
layers of newspaper – they should keep warm for a few hours.

10 MARCH

Celebrate the telephone

Today in 1876 the first ever words were spoken on a new
invention, the telephone. Use it as an excuse to have an epic
phone conversation with a friend.

11 MARCH

Cruft's dog show

Cruft's is the biggest dog show in the world. It
takes place around this date for four days every
year. So why not...

TEACH YOUR DOG TO SIT

For this to work well, you and your dog should both be in a good mood, with plenty of time on your hands. Don't get frustrated if your dog doesn't get it right at first – dogs are easily confused and they can be slow learners, but they are very eager to please. You will need dog treats to tempt your dog with, so it's not a good idea to try this straight after feeding time.

1. Call your dog to you. Show him the treat at nose height and raise it over his head and towards his back.

2. Your dog should sit down naturally at this point – just before he does, say, 'Sit!' in a clear voice.

3. Give your dog the treat and lots of praise.

4. If your dog backs away instead of sitting, try again, this time with your dog standing with his back to a corner.

5. Keep going for about five minutes – any longer and one or both of you might get bored.

If you don't have a dog, try training your cat/goldfish/little brother.

12 MARCH
Saint Gregory's Day

Saint Gregory's Day is traditionally said to be a good day to plant onions. Buy some seeds (they are very cheap) and grow some veg.

13 MARCH
Discovery of Uranus

On this day in 1781 William Herschel discovered the planet Uranus. To celebrate...

Go star spotting

Spend the day with a book, learning about constellations, and the evening spotting some.

Here are some easy ones you can look for:

Ursa Minor (Little Bear)

Ursa Major (Great Bear)

14 March
Pi Day

The Greek letter π or pi, (pronounced pie) in the Greek alphabet, is the maths symbol for the ratio of the circumference of a circle to its diameter. Maths fans get excited about it because it's an irrational number – that means the digits go on forever without repeating. It's equal to 3.1415926535... and goes on and on. Pi day is celebrated today because (in the US) 14 March is often written as 3.14. People celebrate by eating pie (known as pi pie), often decorated with a Greek letter pi or even some of the digits.

Computers have calculated the value of pi to over 1 trillion digits after the decimal point and some people pride themselves on how many digits they can remember. The world record holder is Chao Lu from China. He took more than 24 hours to repeat 67,890 digits of the number. See how many you can memorize (we don't have room for 67,890 but here are the first 40):

3.1415926535897932384626433832795028841997

Learning this will seriously impress your maths teacher.

15 March
Anniversary of Julius Caeser's death

Ancient Roman ruler Julius Caesar was assassinated on 15 March, 44 BC. To commemorate one of the most famous murders in history, why not learn how to think like an ancient Roman?

LEARN ROMAN NUMERALS

Thank goodness for decimals. If you were an ancient Roman, you would have to count using this system:

$1 = I$ $5 = V$ $10 = X$ $50 = L$

$100 = C$ $500 = D$ $1,000 = M$

The numbers in between use a combination of these numerals. A smaller numeral in front of a larger one means you subtract the smaller number from the larger one. A larger numeral followed by a smaller one means you add the numbers together. Here are some examples:

$$III = 3$$
$$VII = 5 + 2 = 7$$
$$IX = 10 - 1 = 9$$
$$XV = 10 + 5 = 15$$
$$XL = 50 - 10 = 40$$
$$LX = 50 + 10 = 60$$
$$CL = 100 + 50 = 150$$

If you want bigger numbers, a line on top of a numeral multiplies it by 1,000. For example:

$\overline{V} = 5,000$ $\overline{L} = 50,000$

$\overline{C} = 100,000$ $\overline{M} = 1,000,000$

16 MARCH (March or April)
Mother's Day

This falls on a Sunday between 1 March and 4 April. On Mother's Day, why not get up early for a change and make your mum a special breakfast in bed? An even better Mother's Day gift idea is a number of pieces of paper with 'I owe you…' written on them. You could owe your mum a morning's housework, a home-made lunch, or a gardening job. It's up to your mum when she calls in her 'debts'.

17 MARCH
Saint Patrick's Day

Wear a shamrock, or something green to celebrate Ireland's patron saint. You could also take the opportunity to impress everyone with your astounding knowledge about Saint Patrick, who wasn't Irish (he was either English or Scottish), but became enslaved by an Irish chieftain. He escaped and went home, but later returned to Ireland and became a priest.

18 MARCH
First space walk

On 18 March 1965, cosmonaut Aleksei Leonov made the first ever space walk. To commemorate his achievement, find out as much as you can about the solar system.

SOLAR SYSTEM QUIZ:

1. Which is the third planet from the Sun?

2. An asteroid belt lies between Mars and which other planet?

3. Which planet was demoted to a dwarf planet in 2006?

4. How many planets are there in our solar system?

5. How often is Halley's Comet visible from Earth?

6. What's the difference between a meteor and a meteorite?

Answers: 1)Earth; 2)Jupiter; 3)Pluto; 4)Eight; 5)Once every 75/76 years; 6) Meteors are shooting stars — space debris burning up in the atmosphere. Meteorites are bits of space debris that make it through the atmosphere and fall to Earth.

59

19 MARCH

David Livingstone's birthday

Famous explorer, Dr David Livingstone, was born today in 1813. To celebrate try some exploration of your own...

FIND NORTH WITHOUT USING A COMPASS

• Put a stick in the ground and measure its shadow at different times of day. The shortest shadow will point north (or, if you're in the southern hemisphere, it will point south).

• Find the North Star, Polaris, which points north (in the northern hemisphere). Or, in the southern hemisphere, find the constellation the Southern Cross, which points roughly south.

• Look at trees: they tend to have fewer branches, and more moss and lichen, on the side facing north.

• Use your watch as a compass (see 6 June).

20 MARCH

Anniversary of the Theory of Relativity

On 20 March 1905, Einstein published his book The Foundation of the General Theory of Relativity. In his book, Einstein pondered travelling at the speed of light, and ended up changing the world as a result. You can read all about

Einstein and his amazing life in **Horribly Famous: Einstein and his Inflatable Universe** by Mike Goldsmith.

21 MARCH
The first day of spring

Does your room smell of spring flowers or old trainers? Keep it smelling sweet for longer by putting bunches of dried lavender and rosemary in a covered bowl with some dried rose petals (see page 115). Give the bowl a shake every so often. Take off the cover and you have your own potpourri.

22 MARCH
First English football league

The English football league was formed on 22 March 1888. Get together with nine friends and have your own five-a-side soccer match today. Remember that in five-a-side football, the ball shouldn't go above head height, and if the pitch is enclosed you can kick the ball against the side walls and carry on playing.

23 MARCH
The Tubilustrium

If you were an ancient Roman, you might want to purify your war trumpet today. The Tubilustrium was the festival marking the Army's preparations for war, beginning with a special indoor ceremony to purify the army's trumpets, during which a lamb was sacrificed. Outside, 12 dancing priests called

Sulii went singing and dancing through the streets of Rome. Play a wind instrument today (even if it's just a recorder) to remember the Ancient Roman trumpet festival.

24 MARCH
Harry Houdini's birthday

Harry Houdini, magician and escapologist, was born on 24 March 1874. He was very sceptical of 'mind readers' who claimed to have supernatural powers. Wow your friends by learning to...

PERFORM A MIND-READING TRICK

Explain how you did the trick afterwards, though, as Houdini would have wanted.

1. Look in a large book (a telephone book, or a dictionary) at page 108, and write down the ninth entry on that page on a piece of paper and put it in a sealed envelope.

2. Gather your audience. Give the sealed envelope to a volunteer, and give the book to a different volunteer.

3. Ask three different members of the audience for a different number between one and nine, and write each number down in order on a blackboard or a large piece of paper so that the whole audience can see.

4. Ask your first volunteer to reverse the three-digit number. Now get them to subtract the bigger number from the smaller one. (So if the number's 751, reverse it to get 157, then subtract 157

from 751 to get 594.) You might need to give them a calculator, or at least a pen and paper.

5. Ask your volunteer to take this new number (594), then reverse the digits (to get 495), and add the two together (to get 1089).

6. Now ask your volunteer to look at the first three digits of the number (108) and turn to that page in the book. Then count down to the ninth entry and read the word aloud.

7. Call for the person with the sealed envelope to open it and read the word on the paper aloud.

8. Bask in the applause. Then explain that the trick always works because the number will always be 1089, no matter which three digits are called out, and give some examples.

25 MARCH

National Day in Greece

Why not celebrate by making this simple and delicious Greek dish?

MAKE TZATZIKI

YOU NEED: 350 g Greek yoghurt; 1 medium cucumber; 2 cloves of garlic, chopped; 30 ml lemon juice; a little olive oil; mint leaves

1. Peel the cucumber, cut it in half lengthways and take out the seeds, then chop finely.
2. Put the chopped cucumber in a tea towel and squeeze it to drain all the excess liquid.
3. Mix the cucumber with the yoghurt, garlic and lemon juice.
4. Drizzle a little olive oil on top, and add the mint leaves.

26 MARCH
Leonard Nimoy's birthday

Leonard Nimoy, actor and director, was born on 26 March 1931. He's most famous for his performance in the Star Trek TV series and films as Mr Spock. Wear a pair of Vulcan ears in his honour today.

27 MARCH
The first international rugby match

The first ever international rugby match was played on 27 March 1871 between England and Scotland. If you don't play already, why not give it a go?

Here are a few basics of Rugby Union...

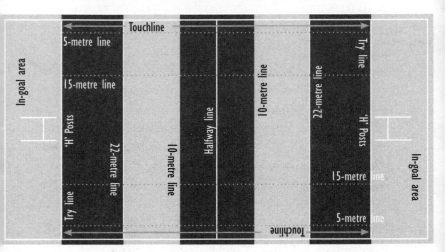

THE BASICS
- Each team has 15 players, with up to seven replacement players.
- The aim is to score as many points as possible by the end of the 80-minute game, which is split into two 40-minute halves.
- The game starts with a kick from the centre of the pitch into the opposing team's half – the ball must travel at least 10 metres into the other team's half of the pitch.
- Each team tries to move the ball towards the opposing team's try line. Players can run with the ball and pass it backwards – but not forwards – to team-mates. They can also kick the ball forwards.

• A player in possession of the ball can be tackled physically and brought to the ground – at which point, the tackled player should release the ball.

SCORING
• A try – a player touches the ball to the ground over the opposing team's try line. This is worth five points.
• A conversion – after a try, a player from the team who won the try attempts to kick the ball over and between the goal posts. This is worth two points.
• A drop goal – a player running with the ball drops it on the ground then kicks it over and between the goalposts after it has bounced once. This is worth three points.
• If a ball is kicked over the touchline, the defending team is given a line-out: between three and eight players from each team line up parallel to one another, while the ball is thrown in by a player from the defending team. All players in the line-out try to grab the ball.
• If the rules are broken (for example, if the ball is passed forwards rather than backwards), eight players from each team interlock to form a 'scrum'. The ball is rolled in to the middle of the scrum and players must compete for it using their feet. Players have to stay in the scrum until the ball has come out.

28 MARCH
Something-on-a-Stick Day
In the US, today is the day to celebrate food on a stick. Have an ice lolly – or a kebab – to celebrate.

29 MARCH

Space Probe lands on Mercury

On 29 March 1974, the space probe Mariner 10 visited Mercury and sent back images of planet's surface. Impress your friends with your amazing interplanetary knowledge.

In our solar system, Mercury is the closest planet to the Sun and also the smallest – it's less than half the size of Earth.

During the day, the temperature is a blistering 430°C.

At night it's a bit chilly: minus 170°C.

Heat from the Sun is intense because of Mercury's thin atmosphere.

It takes Mercury 88 Earth days to orbit the Sun, so a year on Mercury lasts 88 Earth days.

A Mercury day is about 59 Earth days long. This is because Mercury takes 59 days to revolve once on its axis.

Mercury is named after the Roman messenger god.

30 March
Vincent van Gogh's birthday

The famous artist Vincent van Gogh was born today in 1853. One of his most famous paintings is called **Sunflowers**. Try painting or drawing your own – it doesn't have to look anything like the famous painting. You could make it out of real sunflower seeds (or just use the seeds for the middle).

31 March
Oranges and lemons

On the last day of March, primary school children gather at the church of Saint Clement Danes in London, UK, where they recite this rhyme:

'Oranges and lemons,' say the bells of Saint Clement's.
'I owe you five farthings,' say the bells of Saint Martin's.
'When will you pay me?' say the bells of Old Bailey.
'When I grow rich,' say the bells of Shoreditch.
'When will that be?' say the bells of Stepney.
'I do not know,' says the great bell of Bow.

The children each receive an orange and a lemon. Celebrate yourself by making a Saint Clement's drink. Mix equal parts of orange juice and lemonade and serve with ice cubes and a slice of lemon.

1 APRIL
April Fool's Day

Here are a few simple practical jokes you could play on your friends...

• Glue a long, thin piece of thread to a coin and place the coin on the ground. Wait round the corner with the other end of the thread. Just as someone bends down to pick up the coin, give the thread a yank.

• Put a piece of clear sticky tape over the keyhole on your front door and await your first victim.

• Put golden syrup on a door handle. Whoever touches it will be horrified until they find out what it is. You could be generous and tell them ... after a couple of hours.

2 APRIL
Taily Day

This is the Scottish version of April Fool's Day – choose another practical joke! This time you can really surprise someone...

3 APRIL
National Chocolate Mousse Day

Believe it or not, in the US today really is National Chocolate Mousse Day. There really is only one way to celebrate. Yum!

4 APRIL
Feast Day of Saint Isidore

Saint Isidore is the patron saint of the Internet – the perfect excuse to spend some time using it. Why not design your own website or start a blog?

5 APRIL
Cold food festival

In China, today is the start of the cold food festival, which lasts for three days. People observing the festival only eat uncooked food. Eat salad today – it might make up for all the chocolate mousse you scoffed two days ago.

6 APRIL
Butch Cassidy's birthday

Butch Cassidy, cowboy turned bank robber, was born today in 1866. So why not learn an old cowboy skill and...

MAKE A LASSO

YOU NEED: a long rope; a needle and thread

1. Make a small loop in the end of the rope, big enough for the rope to pass through (but not much bigger).

2. Wrap the very end of the rope round the loop a couple of times and sew it in place. You now have a length of rope with a small loop (called a 'honda') in the end.

3. Pass the free end of the rope through the honda to make a big loop. Gather the rest of the rope in your other hand.

4. Now see if you can lasso something. It might be best to start with a fence post, rather than something that can actually move.

7 April
William Wordsworth's birthday

Today is the birthday of poet William Wordsworth, who was born in 1770. One of his most famous poems, 'I Wandered Lonely as a Cloud' or 'Daffodils', is especially appropriate at this time of year because the first Sunday in April is known as Daffodil Sunday. In the nineteenth century, people would wear daffodils and give them as gifts. Wear your own daffodil today, or make up a poem … or both.

8 April (between late March and late April)
Good Friday

The Christian festival of Easter can fall on any Sunday between 22 March and 25 April. Hot cross buns are traditionally eaten on the Friday before Easter, Good Friday, but since they're tasty at any time of year, why not spend today making (and eating) this delicious Easter treat?

MAKE HOT CROSS BUNS

YOU NEED: 50 g sugar; 150 ml warm water; 1 tbsp dried yeast; 450 g plain flour; 1 tsp salt; 1 tsp mixed spice; 75 g currants; 50 g mixed peel; 50 ml warm milk; 50 g melted butter; 1 egg; 1 large, greased polythene bag; greased baking sheet

1. Make the yeast mixture: mix a teaspoon of sugar with the warm water, then sprinkle in the yeast. Put it to one side while you get on with the next bit.

2. Sift the flour, salt and mixed spice into a bowl. Then add the rest of the sugar, the currants and mixed peel. Make a dip in the middle of the mixture.

3. Once the yeast mixture has become frothy, pour it into the middle of the flour mixture along with most of the milk, the melted butter and the egg.

4. Mix it all together to form a dough. Add extra milk if it looks dry. Take it out of the bowl and knead it for five minutes.

5. Put the dough back into the bowl and put the whole thing inside the polythene bag. Put it somewhere warm to rise for about an hour.

6. When the dough has doubled in size, take it out of the bowl and knead it again until it's back to its original size.

7. Divide the dough into 12 balls and put them on the greased baking sheet (don't put them too close together). Cut a deep cross on the top of each one with a sharp knife.

8. Cover with the polythene bag and leave them somewhere warm for about 30 minutes. Preheat the oven to 220°C/ gas mark 7.

9. When the buns have risen, put them in the oven for about 15 minutes or until they are golden brown.

10. Invite some friends over and eat them.

9 APRIL (the whole month of April)
Scarecrow festival

Every April, the village of Moringhem in France hosts its annual scarecrow festival. Villagers put scarecrows outside their homes to amuse or terrify passers by, and at the end, the King of the Scarecrows is burnt on a bonfire. Spend today making your own scarecrow to keep birds off the vegetable patch – add shiny things like old CDs to catch the light, and hang some metal objects from it – they'll make a noise when the wind blows.

10 APRIL
Titanic sets sail

On this day in 1912, the ship RMS Titanic set off on its fateful voyage across the Atlantic. So perhaps this is a good day to stay at home. Whatever happens, stay away from water ... and especially icebergs.

11 APRIL (late March to late April)
Easter Sunday

Easter Sunday can fall any time between 22 March and 25 April. Most people are familiar with chocolate Easter eggs, but decorating chickens' eggs is a much older (and less fattening) tradition...

DECORATE AN EASTER EGG

In the old days, people made a pinhole in an egg and sucked out the insides ... you might want to hard boil yours (boil them for 7–10 minutes). Don't eat the egg after decorating it, though. Here are some egg-decorating ideas...

• Paint your egg with acrylic paint – coloured dots look good. Or draw on a face – a clown's, perhaps?
• You can also colour your egg by mixing a teaspoon of food colouring with two teaspoons of vinegar in a cup big enough to hold your egg. Half fill the cup with water, stir, and carefully drop in your egg. The longer you leave it, the darker the colour will be.
• Glue sequins, glitter, and ribbon onto coloured eggs for a bit of added sparkle.

12 APRIL
First person in space

Today in 1961, Soviet cosmonaut Yuri Gagarin became the first person to travel into space. To celebrate…

MAKE YOUR OWN
FIZZ-PROPELLED ROCKET

YOU NEED: A4 paper; photographic film canister (not many people use these any more but you could ask at a photographic shop – the lid should fit inside the canister); sticky tape; water; fizzy antacid tablet; paper towel

1. Prepare your launch site somewhere outside where there are no small children or pets.

2. Tape a canister, end down, to the long edge of your paper. Roll the paper up to make a tube.

3. You could make a nose cone and fins for your rocket out of another sheet of paper, or you could just leave it as a tube.

4. Fill the canister with water until it's about a third full.

5. Put the antacid tablet into the canister, quickly replace the lid, and stand the rocket on your lauchpad.

6. Watch your rocket zoom into space   or at least a few

13 APRIL
Songkran
On the first full moon in April, Thai Buddhists celebrate their New Year by having a massive water fight during the festival of Songkran. People arm themselves with buckets, bottles and water pistols. Celebrate Songkran by having your own water fight.

14 APRIL
Happy New Year!
As in Thailand (see 13 April), lots of countries celebrate the New Year on or around 14 April – India, Nepal, Sri Lanka, Cambodia, Laos and Myanmar, for example. Celebrate with them and have a New Year party. In Cambodia, the New Year cake (kralan) is made with rice, beans and coconut, so make sure you have plenty of coconut cake at your celebration.

15 APRIL
International Kite Festival
The biggest kite festival in Europe is held around the middle of April every year in Berck sur Mer in France. Find a windy spot and fly a kite today.

16 APRIL
Wilbur Wright's birthday
Wilbur Wright was born today in 1867. He and his brother built the first aeroplane that actually flew. Why not...

FLY A PAPER PLANE

YOU NEED: a sheet of A4 paper

1. Fold the paper in half and open it out again. Fold the two top corners into the centre.

2. Fold the two top corners into the centre again.

3. Turn the paper over, and fold the two top corners into the centre and then unfold them.

4. Pinch the centre fold between your thumb and forefinger, and then turn the paper over to reveal your plane.

5. To fly it, hold it between your thumb and forefinger a few centimetres from the nose and throw it gently, overarm.

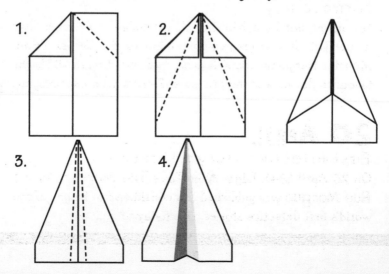

17 APRIL
The Simpsons' birthday
Today is the anniversary of the first ever episode of The Simpsons, shown in 1987. Spend the day drawing your own cartoon strip, or even creating your own animated cartoon (use a computer, or make a flick book with a notepad).

18 APRIL
Pet Owner's and Crossword Puzzle Day
In the US, today is both Pet Owner's Day and Crossword Puzzle Day. So give your pet (if you have one) a special treat today — perhaps while doing a crossword. Or try making up your own pet-themed crossword. Make up some fiendishly difficult clues and try it out on your family.

19 APRIL
Primrose Day
You might not have heard of it, but today is Primrose Day in the UK. It was created to remember the British Prime Minister Benjamin Disraeli, who died on 19 April 1881. His favourite flower was the primrose. Plant a primrose today.

20 APRIL
First detective story published
On 20 April 1841, Edgar Allan Poe's The Murders in the Rue Morgue was published. It's considered to be one of the world's first detective stories. Use today to...

WRITE YOUR OWN DETECTIVE STORY

HERE ARE A FEW TIPS:

• Work out your plot. You won't have much of a detective story without a good one. What type of crime has been committed? Murder or theft (of the world's biggest diamond, or a great work of art) are popular choices. Why was the crime committed?

• Who committed the crime? Ensure it's not obvious who your criminal is. Perhaps it's someone inconspicuous, or someone who seems completely honest at first.

• Scatter some red herrings and clues so that the reader can try to beat the detective to his or her conclusion.

• Since your detective is the main character, make him or her interesting and believable. Why did they become a detective? Do they have any character flaws or qualities that might lead them to the wrong or right conclusions?

• Try to provide a twist at the end of the tale. For example, does the detective discover with horror that the wrong person has gone to prison once it's too late?

21 APRIL
Queen Elizabeth II's birthday

Why not hold a garden party? Provide cucumber sandwiches (with the crusts cut off, naturally), gallons of tea and plenty of cake. Swan about pretending to be very posh and play croquet on the lawn.

22 APRIL
Earth Day

Every 22 April people celebrate planet Earth and wonder how we might do a better job of looking after it in the future. Celebrate by gathering a group of friends and mounting a rubbish clearing mission on a local green space. You'll be amazed at how much difference you can make in just a couple of hours.

23 APRIL
Talk Like Shakespeare Day

Today is probably William Shakespeare's birthday (nobody is quite sure), and also the date of his death. Spend today talking like Shakespeare, saying 'prithee' and 'hey nonny no' a lot and addressing people as 'thou'. You could also celebrate Saint George's Day, England's national day.

24 April
Saint Mark's Eve

According to superstition, if you want to see your future husband or wife, tonight is the night to do it. Boys and girls who walk around their local church looking out of each window in turn should see their future partner in the last window. Another scarier superstition says that anyone who keeps watch at the church on Saint Mark's Eve will see all of the local people who are to die that year.

25 April
World Penguin Day

On the 25 April every year, the Adélie penguins in the Antarctic begin their annual northward migration – or around about then, anyway, since penguins don't have calendars. In honour of this event, 25 April is World Penguin Day. You could celebrate by dressing in black and white and waddling around like a penguin for the day.

26 APRIL
John J Audobon's birthday

Naturalist John J Audobon, born on 26 April 1785, catalogued the birds of North America. In his honour, make a pine-cone bird feeder. Coat a pine cone in peanut butter, roll it in birdseed, and hang it from a tree branch with string.

27 APRIL
Samuel Morse's birthday

On 27 April 1791, Samuel Morse, inventor of Morse Code, was born. What better time to learn Morse Code – you never know, it could come in handy...

A ._	H	O ___	V ..._
B _...	I ..	P .__.	W .__
C _._.	J .___	Q __._	X _.._
D _..	K _._	R ._.	Y _.__
E .	L ._..	S ...	Z __..
F .._.	M __	T _	
G __.	N _.	U .._	

28 APRIL
National Blueberry Pie Day

People in the US celebrate all kinds of different food days, some of them more appealing than others. Have a go and learn how to...

MAKE A BLUEBERRY PIE

YOU NEED: 400 g shortcrust pastry; 600 g blueberries; 120g caster sugar; 1 tbsp water; 20cm pie dish; 1 tbsp milk

1. Put the blueberries in a pan with the sugar and water and heat gently. Simmer for a couple of minutes.

2. Divide the pastry into two pieces, one slightly bigger than the other.

3. Roll out the base to the correct size and place it in the pie dish. Add the blueberry mixture.

4. Roll out a circle for the top. Place it on top of the pie. Seal the top to the base using a fork.

5. Brush the top with milk and make a few cuts in it.

6. Place in a oven preheated to 190°C/ gas mark 5 for 30 minutes.

7. Wait for it to cool completely before cutting yourself a large slice.

29 APRIL
International Dance Day
Spend today improving your dance skills – or learning a new dance.

30 APRIL

May Day Eve
Tonight used to be considered the favourite night for witches to ride and meet, rather than Halloween. Have a May Day Eve spooky party – get your guests to wear their Halloween costumes and tell ghost stories.

1 MAY
May Day

As well as dancing around the maypole on your village green, you might like to try an old May Day beauty treatment. When you wake up, rush outside and wash your face in the dew on the grass. People used to believe that May dew is magic, and anyone who washes their face in it will have a beautiful complexion throughout the year ahead.

2 MAY
David Beckham's birthday

David Beckham was born on 2 May 1975. So today is a good day to practise your football skills...

PENALTY TAKING TIPS

• Decide where you're going to kick the ball and stick to it.

• For the best chance of scoring a goal with your penalty kick, aim high and to the right or left. Aiming low and for the middle gives the goalkeeper the best chance of saving the penalty.

• If you kick the ball with your laces, the shot will be more powerful, or you could use the side of your foot to achieve a more accurate shot.

3 MAY
Get gardening

Unless it's still frosty where you live, today's a good day to plant out some herbs such as basil and coriander. They won't survive in the winter but they should last you all summer. Buy small packets of herb seeds and plant them in compost in a recycled container (an old margarine tub is perfect). Make sure you add some drainage holes. Keep your herb pots somewhere sunny and give them plenty of water.

4 MAY (May)
Go cheese rolling

Every year in May, contestants gather to race down a massively steep hill after a piece of cheese, in the annual Gloucester Cheese

Rolling. There are various cheese rolling events in England – the one in Gloucestershire takes place at Cooper's Hill. If you can't make it to Gloucestershire, get in touch with your inner small child and roll (sideways) down a hill until you get dizzy.

5 MAY
Cinco de Mayo

The **Cinco de Mayo** (Spanish for 5 May) is a holiday in Mexico and the US remembering the Battle of Puebla. Today, it's celebrated with music, dancing, and food. Celebrate yourself, and...

MAKE MEXICAN BEAN SALAD

YOU NEED: 3 eggs, hard-boiled; 2 avocados, sliced; 1 x 400 g tin of red kidney beans; 1 x 400 g tin of chickpeas; 250 g tomatoes, chopped; 1 small red onion, sliced; 1 red chilli, chopped; bunch of coriander, chopped; 2 tbsp salad dressing; 1/2 tsp cumin

1. Cut the eggs into quarters and put them in a bowl with the avocados, beans, onion, coriander and tomatoes.

2. Add the chilli and the cumin powder and mix it all together with the dressing.

3. Eat with pitta bread or flour tortillas.

6 MAY
The Penny Black's birthday
On 6 May 1840 the world's first stamp, the Penny Black, went on sale. Send a postcard to someone today.

7 MAY (first Friday in May)
No Pants Day
Don't be alarmed: this is the American definition of pants, so it means trousers – not underwear. People have walked around trouserless on the first Friday in May for many years in celebration of this strange unofficial holiday. Why not join them? You might want to limit this to the privacy of your own home, though!

8 MAY
No Socks Day
Believe it or not, No Socks Day follows No Pants Day. Give your toes a breather today. Paint your toenails, since they're going on display. Draw some attention to them by making them multicoloured.

9 MAY
J M Barrie's birthday
The writer of **Peter Pan**, J M Barrie, was born today in 1860. Celebrate the boy who never grew up by doing a few things adults could never get away with.

· *Walk along the top of a wall*

· *Ride a donkey or build a sandcastle on the beach*

· *Make a fort out of cardboard boxes*

· *Play hopscotch.*

10 MAY

Emperor Claudius Gothicus' birthday

Celebrate the birth of this ancient Roman back in AD 213 by learning the Roman days of the week – then impress your history teacher...

DIES LUNAE	MONDAY
DIES MARTIS	TUESDAY
DIES MERCURIS	WEDNESDAY
DIES IOVIS	THURSDAY
DIES VENERIS	FRIDAY
DIES SATURNI	SATURDAY
DIES SOLIS	SUNDAY

11 May

Salvador Dali's birthday

The famous surrealist artist Salvador Dali was born today in 1904. Celebrate by creating your own surrealist collage. Surrealists liked putting lots of random things together to look like a weird dream. Place together (for example) a picture of a badger, Queen Elizabeth I, the Empire State Building and a bunch of roses. Or take an image of a bunch of flowers and replace the flower heads with farm animals. Let your imagination go wild...

12 May

Edward Lear's birthday

Edward Lear, writer of nonsense poems, was born today in 1812. He's most famous for writing 'The Owl and the Pussycat' and his limericks, like this one:

> *There was an old man with a beard,*
> *Who said, 'It is just as I feared!*
> *Two owls and a hen,*
> *Four larks and a wren,*
> *Have all built their nests in my beard!'*

Why not have a go at making up your own limerick today?

13 MAY (nearest Sunday)
Rook Sunday

The nearest Sunday to 13 May was known as Rook Sunday. You probably won't want to try the food traditionally eaten today: rook pie. Have some apple pie instead.

14 MAY
Dance Like a Chicken Day

There is only one way to celebrate – forget about looking cool and get dancing – or should that be flapping?

15 MAY
Andy Murray's birthday

Scottish tennis player Andy Murray was born today in 1987. It's time to get out your tennis racket and start practising, ready for Wimbledon fortnight.

16 May
Sea-Monkey Day
Sea-Monkeys aren't monkeys at all. They are tiny shrimp-like creatures that come to life when they're put in water. The creatures hatch in a matter of hours, and can grow to be a couple of centimetres long. Get a fish bowl and buy a Sea-Monkey kit today.

17 May
Anniversary of Botticelli's death
Italian painter Sandro Botticelli died today in 1510. So, today's the perfect day to get your friends together and…

PLAY BOTTICELLI

YOU NEED: at least three players

1. One player thinks of a famous person and tells the other players the initial letter of the famous person's surname.

2. The other players take it in turn to ask the first player a question with a yes/no answer about the famous person.

3. Play continues until someone correctly guesses the famous person.

18 MAY (mid-May)

Water Jousting Championships

Around this time every year, the town of Saint-Raphael in France holds its water jousting championships, which consists of people in boats trying to knock one another into the water with oars. If it's a warm day, have a water balloon fight with your friends.

19 MAY

Anniversary of Anne Boleyn's death

Anne Boleyn, second wife of King Henry VIII of England, had her head chopped off on 19 May 1536. So remember Henry VIII's wives and what happened to them with this...

ROYAL RHYME

Divorced, Beheaded, Died
Divorced, Beheaded, Survived

1. **Catherine of Aragon (Divorced)**
2. **Anne Boleyn (Beheaded)**
3. **Jane Seymour (Died)**
4. **Anne of Cleves (Divorced)**
5. **Katherine Howard (Beheaded)**
6. **Catherine Parr (Survived)**

20 MAY (mid to late May)
Scorton Silver Arrow

The world's longest established sporting event takes place in mid to late May in Yorkshire, and has been held since the Society of Archers was formed in 1673. Go along and watch archers compete for the Silver Arrow prize, or have a go at firing an arrow yourself. If you can't arrange an archery lesson, have a game of darts instead.

21 MAY
Mary Anning's birthday

Mary Anning, fossil collector and palaeontologist, was born on 21 May in 1799, so...

MAKE YOUR OWN FOSSIL

Choose an object you want to make into a fossil – perhaps a small plastic toy. Make sure you get an adult to help you with this.

YOU NEED: your object; a shallow plastic or cardboard box, big enough for your object; plaster of Paris; petroleum jelly

1. Make up the plaster of Paris following the instructions on the pack and pour it into the box.

2. Coat your object in petroleum jelly and half submerge it in the plaster of Paris.

3. Leave it to harden somewhere warm.

4. When the plaster of Paris is hard, remove the object.

5. The box will look as though it contains a real fossil.

22 MAY
Arthur Conan Doyle's birthday

Arthur Conan Doyle, most famous for his Sherlock Holmes detective stories, was born today in 1859. Learn a detective skill – with a friend, try lifting wet footprints with some kitchen roll and matching them to the shoes that made them.

23 MAY

Anniversary of Captain Kidd's death

On 23 May 1701, Captain Kidd was hanged for piracy and murder – even thought he was probably innocent. In memory of this grisly event, why not...

Make your own pirate name

Choose a name from each of the lists below, or create a random pirate name by throwing a dice three times and selecting the names with the corresponding numbers. For example, rolling a two, a one and a six would give you the name Mad Pete Flint.

1. Captain	1. Pete	1. Diamond
2. Mad	2. Gerty	2. Hook
3. Pillaging	3. Jim	3. Diamond
4. Peg-leg	4. Moll	4. Sparrow
5. Salty	5. Tom	5. Silver
6. Cut-throat	6. Peggy	6. Flint

24 MAY
First Morse code

Today in 1844 the first public Morse code transmission took place. So...

Send an enciphered message

This is known as the pigpen cipher. Instead of letters, substitute the box containing the letter. See if you can work out what this message says:

Now send some enciphered messages of your own.

Answer: Meet me at midnight.

25 MAY
Tap Dance Day

In the US, today is National Tap Dance Day. Put on some hard-soled shoes, find a hard floor and get tapping. Start by tapping on the floor with the ball of your foot. Try to make a single, clear sound with each tap, and see how fast you can do it. Keep practising and soon you'll be ready for some more complicated moves.

26 MAY

Dracula published

On 26 May 1897, Bram Stoker's **Dracula** was published for the first time. Put on your fangs and cape and read a vampire story today.

27 MAY

Anniversary of Paul Yost's death

Paul Yost, inventor of the modern hot-air balloon, died today in 2007. If you can't go for a balloon ride to marvel at his achievement, try this balloon-based bet. Bet your friends that you can stick a pin into a balloon without bursting it. All you have to do is stick a piece of sticky tape onto the balloon, then push the pin into the balloon, through the sticky tape – the balloon should stay inflated.

28 May
Feast day of Saint Bernard of Menthon
Saint Bernard is patron saint of mountains (Saint Bernard dogs are named after him). Climb a mountain today – or at least a hill.

29 May
Anniversary of the ascent of Mount Everest
On 29 May 1953, Edmund Hillary and Tenzing Norgay became the first people to reach the top of Mount Everest, the world's tallest mountain. Climb another mountain today.

30 May (Spring bank holiday weekend)
The Hunting of the Earl of Rone
Every spring bank holiday weekend at the end of May, The village of Combe Martin in Devon, UK, holds this unusual event. Hundreds of people take part in hunting the Earl of Rone – a man dressed in a sack coat. When they find him, the Earl has to sit backwards on a donkey before being 'killed' and thrown into the sea. No one is sure who the original Earl of Rone was, but it's thought he was the Earl of Tyrone, who fled from Ireland in 1603 and became shipwrecked here.

31 May
National Macaroon Day
There's only one way to celebrate this American holiday. Eat a macaroon today!

1 JUNE

Superman's birthday

On 1 June 1938, Superman made his first ever appearance in Action Comics. To celebrate watch a Superman film – or just wear your underpants over your trousers.

2 JUNE

Festa della Repubblica in Italy

Today Italy celebrates becoming a republic on 2 June 1942. Why not make an easy version of one of Italy's most delicious desserts.

MAKE EASY ICE CREAM

YOU NEED: 15 g caster sugar; 120 ml whole milk; a few drops of vanilla essence; 100 g rock salt; 1 small, resealable food bag (about half a litre); 1 large, resealable bag (2 litres or so); ice cubes

1. Fill the bigger bag half full of ice and add the rock salt.

2. Put the milk, vanilla and sugar into the small bag and seal it. Then put it inside the larger bag, and seal that.

3. Shake the bags for five minutes.

4. Take the smaller bag out, clean the ice and salt off the outside, then open it.

5. Eat the ice cream.

3 JUNE
Festival of Bellona

In ancient Rome, 3 June was the festival of Bellona – the war goddess and wife, or maybe sister, of the war god Mars. Today is a good day to learn the names of some...

Ancient Roman gods and goddesses

The ancient Romans had gods for just about everything , including a goddess of sewers and a god of mildew! It would take ages to learn the names of all of them, so here are some of the most important ones:

JUPITER (top god)

JUNO (Jupiter's wife and Queen of the gods)

MINERVA (warrior goddess of wisdom)

NEPTUNE (god of the sea)

APOLLO (god of the Sun, music, archery)

DIANA (hunter goddess)

BACCHUS (god of wine)

CERES (harvest goddess)

PROSERPINE (Queen of the Underworld)

PLUTO (King of the Underworld)

MARS (god of war)

VENUS (goddess of love and beauty)

VULCAN (blacksmith god of fire and volcanoes)

MERCURY (messenger god)

VESTA (goddess of the home)

4 JUNE
Hug a Cat Day
Apparently, today is the day to give your furry, feline friends a big cuddle.

5 JUNE

National Gingerbread Day

Another national food day, celebrated in the US. Have a go at making your own delicious gingerbread.

MAKE GINGERBREAD MEN

YOU NEED: 350 g plain flour; 175 g soft brown sugar; 100 g butter; 1 egg, beaten; 4 tsp golden syrup; 1 tsp bicarbonate of soda; 1/2 tsp ground ginger; a man-shaped pastry cutter; raisins.

1. Preheat the oven to 180°C/ gas mark 4.

2. With your fingertips, rub together the flour, butter, ground ginger and bicarbonate of soda in a bowl.

3. When the mixture looks like breadcrumbs, add the sugar, syrup and egg. Mix together with a spoon to form a dough.

4. Sprinkle some flour on a work surface and over your rolling pin. Then roll out the dough until it is about a 1/2 cm thick.

5. Cut out the shapes with a pastry cutter and put them on a non-stick baking tray. Add two raisins for eyes.

6. Put them in the oven for 15 minutes.

7. Take the gingerbread men out of the oven and let them cool before scoffing them.

6 June

Captain Robert Falcon Scott's birthday

Captain Scott, explorer of the Antarctic, was born on this day in 1868. In his memory, why not do some exploring of your own? Follow in his footsteps and head south by learning to...

USE YOUR WATCH AS A COMPASS

1. Put your watch in the palm of your hand and point the hour hand towards the Sun.

2. The north-south line is halfway between the hour hand (where the Sun is now) and the number 12 on the watch face.

7 June

Paul Gaugin's birthday

Paul Gaugin, born in 1848, is one of the most famous artists in the world. Celebrate his birthday by making your own art.

Make Life-size Portraits

Make a life-size picture of a friend by getting them to lie down on a big piece of paper and drawing around them. Fill in the outline using brightly coloured paint, and by sticking on photographs, and pictures from magazines and newspapers.

8 June
World Oceans Day

Take a trip to the seaside and build a sandcastle.

TOP SANDCASTLE-BUILDING TIPS

• Don't build your castle too far away from the sea (where it will take longer to get the water you need) or too close to it (where you might be swamped by the tide).

• Use wet sand for your base and work quickly, so that it doesn't dry out.

• Make towers by building up layers of pancake-shaped dollops of wet sand. Use smaller pancakes as you near the top.

• Build up walls in the same way – use wet 'bricks' of sand and build them up to connect your towers.

• Use plastic knives for carving windows and adding details.

• Use shells and pebbles for decoration.

9 JUNE

Celebrate summer

Summer's here ... almost. To cool off, learn how to...

MAKE ICE LOLLIES

YOU NEED: 4 yoghurt pots, washed; 4 lolly sticks; fruit juice

1. Pour the fruit juice into the yoghurt pots until they are half full. Put them in the freezer for 45 minutes.

2. Push a stick into the semi-frozen fruit juice in each pot, then top them up with more juice.

3. Put the pots back in the freezer overnight, or until they are rock solid.

10 JUNE

National Yo-yo Day

Dig out your yo-yo and practise some tricks!

11 JUNE

Kamehameha Day

Today is a national public holiday in Hawaii, USA, celebrating the birthday of King Kamehameha I, who united the Hawaiian islands in the 19th century. It's celebrated with floral parades. Celebrate by making a lei, a Hawaiian symbol of friendship and good luck.

MAKE A LEI

YOU NEED: flowers; a needle; thread

1. Thread your needle.

2. Depending on the flower, either push the needle through the centre or through the stems, and thread them all together.

3. Stop when your lei is long enough to tie around your neck. Traditional leis are about a metre long

12 JUNE (mid-June)

International Viking Festival

Visit the Viking Village near Reykjavik, Iceland, for its annual Viking festival, complete with traditional Viking feasting. If you can't make the festival, you could go on a Viking-style rampage instead.

13 June (mid-June)

World Stinging Nettle Eating Championship

The Bottle Inn in Marshwood, Dorset, UK, holds the World Stinging Nettle Eating Championship every year. Don't try it, they taste awful and can make your taste buds tingle in the worst possible way – painfully. When cooked, nettles can be a tasty, nutritious treat. Simply use the fresh, young leaves in any recipe that uses spinach. Or just steam them and eat them on their own. Don't forget to use gloves when you pick them.

14 June

US Flag Day

Today, Americans celebrate the adoption of the Stars and Stripes on their flag in 1777. Their national anthem, **The Star-Spangled Banner**, is named after it. Learn your own national anthem today – even the second verse. Or you could celebrate with the Americans by learning to sing **The Star-Spangled Banner**.

15 June

Paul Cornu's birthday

Paul Cornu, the French engineer who designed the first helicopter ever to fly, was born today in 1881. Celebrate his birthday and...

MAKE A PAPER HELICOPTER

YOU NEED: a piece of paper measuring 3 cm x 20 cm; scissors; ruler; paperclip

1. Use this template to draw fold lines (the dotted lines) and cut lines (the solid lines) on your strip of paper.

2. Cut the paper along the two cut lines above C and D, and down the cut line between A and B.

3. Fold along the dotted line, 2 cm from the bottom. Fold the flap up.

4. Fold along fold line C. Fold the flap into the centre.

5. Turn the paper over. Fold along fold line D. Fold the flap into the centre.

6. Secure the bottom flaps with a paperclip.

7. Fold flap A towards you. Fold flap B away from you.

8. Throw your helicopter into the air, paperclip end first.

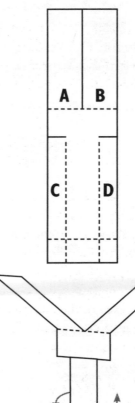

16 JUNE

First woman in space

On 16 June 1963, Valentina Tereshkova became the first woman to enter space. So it's a good day to find out about a few more...

SPACE FIRSTS

1947 – first animals in space (they were fruitflies).

1957 – first artificial satellite, Sputnik 1.

1957 – first animal in orbit, the dog Laika.

1961 – first man in space, Yuri Gagarin.

1963 – first woman in space, Valentina Tereshkova. Valentina went on to have the first baby whose parents had both travelled into space!

1965 – first space walk, Alexie Leonov.

1966 – first spacecraft to land on another planet – Venera 3 landed on Venus.

1966 – first landing on the Moon, by the Luna 9 spacecraft. There were no people on board.

1969 – first man on the Moon, Neil Armstrong.

1971 – first space station, Salyut 1.

1981 – first reusable spacecraft, the Space Shuttle.

1983 – first spacecraft to leave our solar system, the Pioneer 10.

2001 – first space tourist, Dennis Tito.

17 June
Badger Day

Today is the Badger Trust's special Badger Day. To find out more about our black-and-white friends, why not go badger spotting?

• Look out for signs of badger activity, such as footprints in mud. Badgers have five toes with big claws, a large pad behind them.

• Look out for holes in the ground that could be a badger sett.
• When you've found a possible sett, go along just before twilight and wait.

• Make sure you're downwind (badgers have an excellent sense of smell) and hide behind a tree.

• Be very patient.

18 June
Strawberry season

It's strawberry season, so make the most of it. Try dipping strawberries in melted chocolate, or adding a little sugar and cocoa powder to fresh cream for an even sweeter version of strawberries and cream.

19 June

Blooming June

There should be plenty of summer flowers around at this time of year. Save some of them for the winter by learning to...

PRESS FLOWERS

1. Open a big book and lay a sheet of blotting paper inside.

2. Arrange your flowers on one half of the paper and fold the other half over them.

3. Repeat this with more flowers on blotting paper on other pages inside the book if you like. Experiment with lots of different types of flowers.

4. Shut the book, and pile a big stack of heavy books on top.

5. Leave for four weeks before taking out your pressed flowers.

20 June

Father's Day (third Sunday in June)

Don't forget to make your dad a card today. To show him how special you think he is, why not offer to wash the car or take out the rubbish?

21 June

Summer solstice

Today or tomorrow is the longest day of the year (in the northern hemisphere). People flock to the prehistoric site of

Stonehenge in Wiltshire, UK, to watch the Sun rise between the stones. If you can't get there ...

MAKE YOUR OWN STONEHENGE OUT OF BISCUITS

It's a lot easier to build Stonehenge out of biscuits than it was to build it out of stones, but it can be very messy.

YOU NEED: a large tray with low sides; icing sugar; water; 40 shortbread fingers; 40 chocolate fingers; a sharp knife

1. Put the icing sugar in a bowl and add a little water at a time, stirring it until you have a stiff paste. Spread it in a thick layer over the bottom of your tray.

2. Put a little more than half a shortbread finger in the middle, standing on its end. When it was first built Stonehenge consisted of two stone circles, one inside the other, then two horseshoe shapes of stones, one inside the other, with one large stone in the middle.

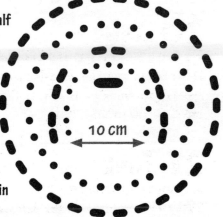

10 CM

3. Cut eight chocolate fingers in half. Arrange 15 of them in a horseshoe shape around the central shortbread. Put them close together. The open end of the horseshoe shouldn't be more than 10 cm, otherwise the outside circle will be too big for your tray.

4. Cut eight shortbread fingers in half. Stand two of the pieces on end, with a third piece across the top (the stone versions of these are called trilithons). Make five 'trilithons' and arrange them in another horseshoe shape just outside the chocolate fingers.

5 Cut 15 chocolate fingers in half. Outside the horseshoe of shortbread, put a circle of 30 halves of chocolate fingers.

6 Cut 30 shortbread fingers in half. Outside the circle of chocolate fingers, make a circle of 30 upright pieces of shortbread. Put one piece of shortbread on top of each pair, to make a continuous circle.

7 Now you just have to eat your biscuit Stonehenge – you might need some help for this!

22 June

National Chocolate Éclair Day

In the US, 22 June is the day for celebrating chocolate éclairs. Eat one today.

23 June

Midsummer's Eve

Make dried rose petals to decorate cards or use as confetti. The simplest way is to take a rose head that's just past its best, leave it in the freezer for a few days, then shake off the petals and let them dry out on kitchen paper. They should keep their colour and shape.

24 June

Midsummer's Day

Pick a rose today: the superstition is that a rose picked today will last until Christmas. (Then freeze it and dry the petals – see 23 June.)

25 June

Fancy footwear

Prepare for the beach by customizing your flip-flops. Glue or sew beads, jewels, glitter, silk flowers, or small plastic toys (little dinosaurs look good) to a pair of cheap, plastic flip-flops, and design your very own unique footwear.

26 JUNE

On 26 June 1483, Richard III was crowned King of England.
Test your historical monarch knowledge with this quiz...

1. King Charles VI of France believed he was made of fudge.

2. King Adolph Frederick of Sweden died after eating 14 helpings of pudding.

3. Queen Joanna of Spain refused to have her dead husband buried and travelled around with the coffin, opening it regularly.

4. Queen Elizabeth I of England often dressed up in a jester's costume.

Answers: 1)False (he believed he was made of glass); 2)True; 3)True; 4)False (she did like to wear a lot of make-up).

27 June

Sunglasses Day

Whatever the weather, wear your favourite pair of shades today. Why not pretend you are hiding from the paparazzi?

28 June (mid to late June)

National Hollerin' Contest

If you feel like shouting very loudly, take part in the National Hollerin' Contest, held every year on the third Saturday in June in North Carolina, USA. There are separate events for young and old, male and female. If you can't make it, hold your own shouting competition with your friends.

29 June

Fruity fun

Make a summer fruit salad with a difference today...

MAKE FRUIT-SALAD ALIENS

• Use oranges, pineapples, grapefruits and apples to make the aliens' bodies. Use cocktail sticks for arms and antennae.

• Use blueberries and other smaller fruit to make eyes and hands. Dried spaghetti makes good hair/bristles, but make sure you take it out before you tuck in.

30 June

Charles Blondin crosses the Niagra falls

On 30 June 1859, the French acrobat Charles Blondin crossed the Niagara Falls on a tightrope. It takes years of practice to learn to tightrope walk, but make a start today by improving your balance skills. Start by walking on stilts (if you can find some), then a beam in a gym. Remember to look where you're going, at eye level — don't look down. Keep your arms out straight. Practise walking from one end of the beam to the other, then standing on one leg.

1 July

International Joke Day

Here are three to pass on to your friends:

• A French cat named Un Deux Trois, and an English cat, named One Two Three, had a swimming race across a pond. Who won?
One Two Thee, because Un Deux Trois Quatre Cinque.

• What do you call someone who's allergic to rice?
Basmatic.

• Why did the man drown in a bowl of muesli?
He was pulled in by a strong currant.

2 July

Anniversary of John Fitch's death

John Fitch, the inventor of the paddle steamer, died today in 1798. So now you have the perfect excuse to...

MAKE YOUR OWN PADDLE-DRIVEN BOAT

YOU NEED: 2 plastic bottles; 2 elastic bands; lolly stick; strong sticky tape

1. Tape the two bottles together and secure one elastic band around the neck ends of the two bottles.

2. Put the lolly stick through the middle of the elastic band. Hold it in place by wrapping the other elastic band around it.

3. Add a little water to each bottle. Put your paddle steamer in a bath (or a pond). Wind up the lolly stick and let it go – the paddle steamer should propel itself across the water. You might need to trim the lolly stick so that it spins freely. Experiment by adding or taking away some water from the bottles so that your boat sits right in the water.

3 July

The start of the Dog Days

According to tradition, today is supposed to be the start of the Dog Days – the 40 hottest days of the summer. Of course, this varies around the world, and in the southern hemisphere, the hottest days summer are between January and March. But if it is summer where you are, today is the day to model your swimwear and decide whether or not it's suitable for public view.

4 JULY
US Independence Day

Most people in the US celebrate with fireworks, but in Lovington, New Mexico, you can go along to their annual 4 July lizard race. If you can't get to a public firework display, or the Lovington lizard race, you could hold a party with some indoor fireworks, or hold your own lizard/slug/snail/woodlouse race.

5 JULY
Anniversary of Nicéphore Niépce's death

Nicéphore Niépce, the French engineer who took the first ever photograph, died today in 1826. His photo was of a view of the countryside taken from a window. Take some photos of what you can see from your bedroom window. You could take a series from different windows – classrooms, coffee shops, buses, trains or cars – and mount an exhibition.

6 July (some time in July)
Boryeong Mud Festival

Every July, tonnes of mud are dumped at Daecheon Beach in South Korea, for its annual mud festival. Watch events including mud-massage, mud-sliding, and a mud-covered human pyramid. Make your own muddy mess today.

7 July
The best day since sliced bread

Otto Frederick Rohwedder, the inventor of the first automatic bread-slicing machine, was born today in 1880. Spend today making some bread.

MAKE BREAD

This is nowhere near as difficult as you might think.

YOU NEED: 500 g strong white flour; 2 tsp salt; 1 x 7 g sachet of fast-acting yeast; ½ tsp salt; 300 ml water; 3 tbsp olive oil.

1. In a large bowl, mix together the flour, salt and yeast.

2. Make a well in the middle of the mixture and add the water and oil. Mix it all together to make a dough (add a little more water if it's a bit stiff).

3. Place the dough on a floured surface and knead until it's smooth.

4. Put the dough in an oiled bowl and leave it somewhere warm to rise until it's doubled in size.

5. Knead the dough until it's back to its original size (this is known as 'knocking back'). Mould it into a ball and put it on a baking tray lined with baking parchment.

6. Leave it to double in size again, then put it in an oven preheated to 220°C/ gas mark 7 for about 25–30 minutes.

7. Remove from the oven when it's golden brown and the loaf makes a hollow sound when you tap its bottom.

8. Eat the bread as soon as it's cool enough.

8 JULY

Anniversary of Roswell

Today is the anniversary of the famous 'Roswell Incident'. This was when 'something' crashed from the sky in 1947 near Roswell in New Mexico, USA, and was widely rumoured to be an alien spacecraft. The US air force claimed it was a weather balloon, but the incident has been the subject of argument ever since. Every year on 8 July, the town of Rosewell holds its UFO Festival. As well as lectures and presentations, there's mud volleyball, an Alien Animal Costume contest, and a UFO parade at the end. If you can't get to Roswell, at least keep an eye out for strange lights in the sky.

9 JULY
Independence Day in Argentina

Today is a good day to learn the countries of South America and impress your geography teacher. Here's a map to help.

1. Argentina
2. Bolivia
3. Brazil
4. Chile
5. Colombia
6. Ecuador
7. French Guiana
8. Guyana
9. Paraguay
10. Peru
11. Suriname
12. Uruguay
13. Venezuela

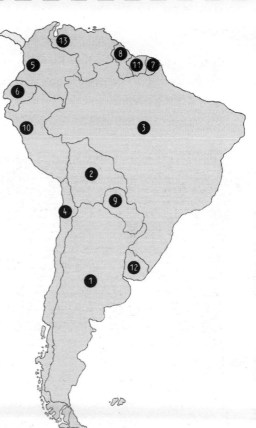

10 July

Teddy Bears' Picnic Day

Today is the day people head to the country, find a quiet spot and eat sandwiches with their stuffed toys. Have a picnic today – with or without your teddy bear. Don't forget to take your favourite sandwiches and, for something a bit different, a thermos flask of gazpacho (Spanish cold soup). Make it by cutting tomatoes, peppers, onion, garlic, cucumber and anything else you fancy into chunks, then whizzing it in a liquidizer. It's like drinking a delicious salad.

11 JULY (various dates in July)
Slug Festival

Go along to the annual slug festival held every year in Eatonville, Washington, USA. The festival celebrates the Northwest banana slug and includes slug races, talks and slimy games. Or find some slugs and hold your own race, today.

12 JULY
Julius Caesar's birthday

The Roman leader Julius Caesar was born today in 100BC. Learn some Latin in his honour – and impress everyone with your amazing knowledge. Here are some Latin phrases that are still used today. See how many you can drop into conversation.

Amor vincit omnia	Love conquers all
Bona fide	In good faith
Carpe diem	Seize the day
Cogito ergo sum	I think therefore I am
Mea culpa	My fault
Non sequitur	It does not follow

Per ardua ad astra	Through hardship to the stars (motto of various air forces)
Tempus fugit	Time flees
Tempus volat hora fugit	Time flies while the hour flees
Vox populi	The voice of the people

13 JULY
Erno Rubik's birthday

Erno Rubik, inventor of the world's best-selling puzzle, the Rubik's Cube, was born today in 1944. Solve a puzzle today – it could be a Rubik's Cube, a jigsaw, a crossword or even a sudoku puzzle.

14 JULY
Bastille Day

Today the French celebrate the storming of the Bastille prison on 14 July 1789, at the start of the French Revolution. In France, they celebrate with military parades, fireworks and parties.

15 July

Saint Swithin's Day

Whatever the weather on Saint Swithin's day, it's supposed to stay that way for the next 40 days. Either celebrate in the sunshine, or buy an umbrella.

16 July

Apollo 11 blasts off

On 16 July 1969, Apollo 11 set off on its mission to land the first human being on the Moon (Neil Armstrong became the first person to set foot on the Moon four days later). Celebrate by checking out some space websites:

www.dailygalaxy.com
www.newscientist.com/section/space
www.space.com
www.hubble.nasa.org
www.nasa.gov

17 July
Get slushy with strawberries
If the weather's hot (or even if it isn't) why not...

MAKE A STRAWBERRY SLUSHY

YOU NEED: a blender; frozen strawberries; ice cubes; fruit juice (any kind you like)

1. Fill the blender about a third full of ice cubes.
2. Add frozen strawberries to almost the maximum level.
3. Top up with fruit juice and blend on the lowest setting.
4. Pour into glasses and toast your friends.

18 July
Swan Upping
Swan Upping on the Thames, between Sunbury and Abingdon in the UK, has been taking place every July since medieval times. 'Swan Uppers' set off in a fleet of small boats and round up the swans, catch them, put rings around their legs, and then release them. Afterwards, a report is made to show how many swans there are on the river, and whether they're healthy. If you can't make it to the Thames, go and feed the swans at a local river or lake.

19 July
The Mary Rose sinks

On 19 July 1545, Henry VIII's warship the **Mary Rose** sank in Portsmouth harbour in the UK. It's since been salvaged, and you can go and see it at Portsmouth Historic Dockyard. Or you could make a paper boat and sail it on a pond or even in the bath...

20 July
Get active

Summer can make you lazy, so get off the sofa and get some exercise. Try playing a game of tag on a jungle gym in a playground – if anyone touches the ground, they become 'It'. Or organize a five-a-side football match (see 22 March) or a game of French cricket (see 5 September).

21 July (every July)
Toe wrestling

Toe wrestling is rather like thumb wrestling – where opponents struggle to pin down the other person's thumb – except with toes. You might not have heard of this unusual sport, but the world championships are held around this date every year in Fenny Bentley, Derbyshire, UK. Gather a group of friends and hold your own championship contest.

22 July
Spoonerism Day

The Reverend William Archibald Spooner was born on 22 July 1844. He was a lecturer at Oxford University in the UK, but he's best known for his habit of confusing words, and saying strange phrases which became known as spoonerisms. Spoonerism Day is held in his honour. Spooner said things like...

> May I sew you to another sheet?
> (May I show you to another seat?)
>
> It is kisstomary to cuss the bride.
> (It is customary to kiss the bride.)

Think of some funny spoonerisms of your own and use them today.

23 July
Neptunalia

The ancient Roman festival of Neptunalia honoured Neptune, god of the sea. Historians think that the ancient Romans probably built huts out of branches and feasted in them. Why not make a den in the woods, or in your back garden, and have a feast in it? Make an indoor one if it's raining.

24 July
Summer holiday

This is one of the best times of year: the start of the summer holidays!

Make a list of all the things you want to do this summer: visit a water park, theme park, or a museum; swim in the sea, fly a kite, have a picnic, etc. See how many you can cross off over the next few weeks.

25 JULY
St James's Day

Build a grotter
To celebrate, take part in an old tradition and build a grotter. A grotter is a hollow mound of mud or sand, decorated on the outside with shells (shells are associated with Saint James). In the evening, candles are lit inside them. The oyster at Whitstable in Kent, UK, has revived the tradition of grotter building. Build one of your own, either at the beach or in the sand pit.

26 JULY
Carl Gustav Jung's birthday
The famous psychologist Carl Jung was born today in 1875. To celebrate Jung's work in the analysis of dreams, use today to...

ANALYSE YOUR DREAMS

Carl Jung made a serious study of dreams and their meanings. Just for fun, see what you think of these dream interpretations.

FLYING DREAMS: flying with ease suggests that you are feeling in control and confident. Difficulties while flying might mean that you lack confidence. If something is hindering your flight (like a mountain), perhaps someone or something is standing in your way in real life?

RUNNING DREAMS: dreams of being chased suggest anxiety in your waking life. Try to work out who or what is chasing you in the dream and see if that person or thing corresponds with something in real life.

FALLING DREAMS: these dreams suggest that you are feeling out of control or anxious in waking life. You might be worried about failing your exams.

DREAMS OF BEING NAKED IN PUBLIC: these are common dreams and suggest that you're feeling vulnerable, or unprepared. Perhaps you have just started a new school, or you're worried that you haven't done enough revision. Or perhaps you're hiding something and you're afraid that other people might find out.

27 July

National Sleepy Head Day

This is celebrated every 27 July in Finland. The last person in the household to wake up is woken up by having water thrown on them — or if the others are feeling really cruel, being thrown into a lake or the sea. Try this out in your own household. In the Finnish city of Naantali, a famous person is chosen every year to be thrown into the sea at 7 am.

28 July

First fingerprint system introduced

On this day in 1901, the first fingerprint system was introduced at New Scotland Yard, the police headquarters in London, UK. Take some for yourself...

TAKE FINGERPRINTS

YOU NEED: talcum powder or cocoa powder; clear sticky tape; paper or card (either white or black to contrast with the powder you've chosen); an ink stamp pad

1. Choose a shiny surface, with some good fingerprints on it, to take your prints from — a glass is perfect.

2. Sprinkle your talc or cocoa powder over the surface as evenly as possible. Blow away excess powder.

3. Stick a piece of sticky tape over the clearest fingerprint. Then carefully remove it.

4. Stick the tape onto your paper or card.

5. Now that you have your print, you need to work out whose it is. Take prints from everyone who's been near the glass. You'll need an inked stamp pad, some willing volunteers, and plenty of patience.

29 JULY
St Olaf's wake

The Faroe Islands celebrate Ólavsøka, or Saint Olaf's wake, on 29 July every year. There's dancing, singing, feasting and the finals of the nation's rowing competition. Find a boating lake and go rowing – have your own competition with your friends.

30 JULY
Henry Moore's birthday

The famous sculptor Henry Moore was born on 30 July 1898. To celebrate, create your own sculpture today. Use air-drying clay, papier-mâché, or even play dough.

31 JULY
JK Rowling's birthday

The Harry Potter author was born today in 1965. Why not try writing your own fantasy novel...

FANTASY WRITING TIPS

• Whether your story is set in Wizard World, the Middle Ages, 21st-century Birmingham or the Land of Dragons, it has to be complete – think about the geography, technology and history of your fantasy world before you start.

• It doesn't matter if your main character is a 20-metre winged dragon – he has to be interesting and believable. Give him a personality.

• Try not to make your plot too much like other famous fantasy novels, so don't include a quest for a ring, or set it in a school for wizards. Try to make up your own story.

AUGUST

1 AUGUST

Lammas

Lammas is a pagan festival marking the death of the corn god. You could celebrate by baking bread (pagans would bake bread in the shape of the corn god, then symbolically sacrifice and eat it). To bring good luck, farmers used to let the first loaf they made go stale, then crumble it in the corners of their barns – you could try crumbling some stale bread around your house for luck.

2 August

Republic Day, Macedonia

Today is Republic Day in Macedonia. Try making a Macedonian national dish...

MAKE TAVCHE GRAVCHE

YOU NEED: 2 x 450 g tins cannellini beans, drained and rinsed; 2 tbsp olive oil; 1 onion, chopped; 1 red pepper, chopped; 1 tsp dried paprika; a handful of fresh parsley and mint, chopped; salt and pepper

1. Preheat the oven to 180°C/ gas mark 4.
2. Heat the oil in a frying pan and add the onion, pepper and dried paprika. Fry for ten minutes.
3. Add the cannellini beans to a casserole dish with some water, the parsley and mint, the fried onion mixture, and some salt and pepper.
4. Bake for about 30 minutes.
5. Enjoy!

3 August

Columbus sets sail

On 3 August 1492, Christopher Columbus set sail on his voyage to find a sea route to China. You could set off on your own voyage of discovery – try a ferry crossing, or a boat trip, if there are no uncharted waters to navigate near you.

4 August

Champagne is invented

Legend has it that the famous sparkling wine, champagne, was invented on 4 August 1693. Celebrate by hearing how to...

MAKE YOUR OWN FIZZY DRINK

YOU NEED: 6 tsp citric acid crystals or powder (available from supermarkets or chemists); 3 tsp bicarbonate of soda; 2 tbsp icing sugar; fruit juice (any kind)

1. Mix the citric acid, bicarbonate of soda and icing sugar together and put it in a jar. Stick a 'fizzy powder' label on it.
2. Put two teaspoons of the powder in a glass and add your juice. You've made your own fizzy drink!

5 August

Neil Armstrong's birthday

It's the birthday of the first person ever to set foot on the Moon. To celebrate, fascinate your friends with these amazing...

MOON FACTS

The Moon is Earth's only natural satellite, and the only celestial body that has been reached by human beings (so far).

The human footprints on the Moon will remain visible for millions of years because there's no wind to blow them away.

The Moon whizzes through space at around 3,600 km/hr, around 384,000 km away from Earth.

A 'blue moon' is the second full moon to occur twice in one calendar month. They're not that unusual – they happen about once every three years.

6 August
Alexander Fleming's birthday

Scientist Alexander Fleming was born on 6 August 1881. He found some mould growing on a Petri dish in his messy lab, and noticed that it had killed the bacteria that had been growing there. This was how he discovered penicillin. So why not...

GROW A BACTERIA COLONY

YOU NEED: Petri dishes; nutrient agar (you can buy this in powder form from a laboratory supplier); cotton buds

1. Make up the nutrient agar following the instructions on the pack and put a thin layer in your Petri dishes.

2. Put a different bacteria source in each Petri dish. For example:

a hair (one of your own), a tiny amount of leftover stew or wipe the inside of the cooker with a cotton bud and then rub it over the surface of your agar.

3. Label the Petri dish lids with the bacteria sources and put them on the dishes.

4. Leave them in a warm place for a day or two.

5. Be horrified at your bacteria colonies.

WARNING: Bacteria is dangerous! Don't remove the lids from the dishes. Ask an adult to remove the lids wearing rubber gloves, and to pour bleach on the agar before throwing them away.

7 August
Birthday of Mata Hari

Mata Hari, the Dutch dancer and spy, was born on 7 August 1876. In celebration of her career in espionage...

MAKE INVISIBLE INK

YOU NEED: lemon juice; a small dish; cotton buds; paper

1. Pour the lemon juice into a small dish.

2. Dip a cotton bud in the juice and use it to write a message on the paper.

3. As the juice dries, the message will disappear.

4. To make it reappear, put the paper against a light bulb (or anything warm) and watch secret messages take shape.

8 AUGUST

Hadrian became emperor

On 8 August AD 117, Hadrian became emperor of Rome. Take a trip to Hadrian's Wall in the north of England and imagine you are trying to fight back the Scots. Alternatively, take this Roman emperor quiz

1. What did the Emperor Hadrian start a fashion for?
a) Flip-flops
b) Beards
c) Handbags for men

2. Which animal did the Emperor Caligula try to give a political role?
a) A dog
b) A monkey
c) A horse

3. Emperor Commodus did which of the following ?
a) He fought as a gladiator
b) He made public appearances completely naked
c) He designed the first hang-glider

Answers: 1)b ; 2)c ; 3)a.

9 AUGUST (late July to late August)
Raksha Bandhan

Raksha Bandhan is a Hindu festival which celebrates the love between brothers and sisters. It falls on the full moon between 23 July and 22 August (which is the Hindu month of Shraavana). Make a special effort to be nice to your brother or sister today – or you could make him/ her a rakhi, a decorated silk thread, which is the traditional gift given on Raksha Bandhan.

10 AUGUST
Magellan sets sail

On 10 August 1519, explorer Ferdinand Magellan set off on his trip to circumnavigate the world (some of his ships made it, though he was killed in a battle in the Philippines). Also, on this day in 1990, the Magellan space probe, named after Ferdinand, reached Venus. To celebrate, learn a few Venusian facts:

• Venus is the second closest planet to the Sun in our solar system and our second closest neighbour (after Mars). It's about the same size as Earth.

• It has huge volcanoes, very high pressure (100 times Earth's), and clouds of sulphuric acid.

• Venus spins around so slowly that one day (the time it takes to spin around on its axis) is longer than one year (the time it takes to orbit the Sun).

11 AUGUST
Feast day of Saint Clare of Assisi

Saint Clare of Assisi is the patron saint of television – yes, honestly. So you now have the perfect excuse if you're not feeling very energetic. Or, if you're feeling more creative, spend the day creating a plan for your own sitcom, documentary or reality TV show.

12 AUGUST
The opening of the Gibson tomb

If you fancy doing something spooky today, you could visit the tomb of the Gibson family at St Nicholas Church, Sutton, UK. Every 12 August it is unlocked and inspected, as it has been since 1793, when the last Gibson died and left money to the local hospital on condition that the tomb should be opened every year. There's a story that if you walk seven times around the tomb a ghost will appear from an urn on its roof. If you can't make it to the Gibson tomb, get your friends together and tell ghost stories. They're scarier if you can set them somewhere near where you live – a graveyard, the woods or a derelict building are all good places to start.

13 AUGUST
International Left-handers' Day

Are you left-handed? Today is the day to remind your right-handed friends of the inconvenience presented to you on a daily basis by things like scissors and tin openers. Remind them of the long list of brilliant left-handers: scientists Marie Curie and Albert Einstein; astronaut Buzz Aldrin; ancient Roman leader Julius Caesar and artists Michelangelo and Leonardo da Vinci are just a few of them.

14 AUGUST

The end of the Second World War

On 14 August 1945 Japan surrendered to the Allies, and the Second World War officially ended. Organize a street party to celebrate, as many people did back in 1945.

- **Make sure the street is closed to cars for the day.**

- **Hang bunting from lampposts.**

- **Put trestle tables down the middle of the street, cover them in paper tablecloths and pile them with party food.**

- **Arrange for a sound system and play cheerful music.**

15 AUGUST

Flooding of the Nile

Today is the start of a two-week holiday in Egypt to celebrate the annual flooding of the River Nile. Ancient Egyptians believed that the Nile was flooded with Isis's tears for her dead husband, Osiris. You could spend today learning some of the many Egyptian gods...

AMUN: represented as a man with a ram's head, and also as a man wearing an ostrich-plumed hat, Amun was a powerful god, known at the height of the Egyptian civilisation as king of the gods.

RA: represented as a man with a hawk's head and disc-shaped headdress, Ra was the Sun god and the most important of all of the Egyptian gods.

ANUBIS: represented as a man with the head of a jackal Anubis was god of embalming and the dead.

BASTET: represented as a woman with a cat's head, Bastet was a protective goddess.

ISIS: represented as a woman with a headdress in the shape of a throne, Isis was an important protective goddess.

OSIRIS: represented as a mummified man with a cone-shaped headdress. Osiris was god of the dead and ruler of the underworld.

16 AUGUST

Rollercoaster Day

It's Rollercoaster Day in the US. If you can't take a ride on a real rollercoaster, try making a model of one instead. Use pipe cleaners or florists' ribbon (which is stiff but bendable). Include plenty of loops and plunging drops.

17 AUGUST

Michael Phelps breaks a record

On 17 August 2008, swimmer Michael Phelps became the first Olympic athlete to win eight gold medals in the same Olympics. Race your friends at your local pool. Or, if swimming's too easy, get out of the pool and...

LEARN HOW TO DIVE

1. Kneel on one knee at the edge of the pool, with your arms stretched over your head, palms downwards, fingers together, and your chin tucked into your chest.

2. Lean forward until your fingers are close to the water.

3. Push off gently with your foot and dive into the water.

4. Once you've got the hang of it, try the same thing standing up, with your toes just over the edge of the pool. Soon you'll be ready for the top board.

18 AUGUST

Get out there

Get a group of friends (ideally, at least 12 of you) and play an outdoor game today...

THE FRISBEE CUP

1. Mark out a pitch at least 50 metres long and 25 metres wide. Mark two goals, six metres or so from each end of the pitch. They should take up the whole width of the pitch at either end.

2. Players divide into two teams and start off in their own goal areas.

3. Toss a coin to see which team throws the Frisbee, aiming for the opposite goal.

4. One or two players remain in their own goal area as defence. The rest pass the Frisbee to one another to try and get it inside the opposing team's goal.

5. A goal is scored when one player successfully passes the Frisbee to another player in his or her team who is inside the goal area of the opposing team.

6. If the Frisbee lands on the ground, or falls outside the pitch, play passes to the other team.

7. Play until one team scores five goals.

19 August
Anniversary of Blaise Pascal's death

Blaise Pascal, mathematician, physicist and philosopher, died today in 1662. His mathematical triangle (known as Pascal's triangle because he was the first person to introduce it) is just one of the clever things he's famous for. Spend some time marvelling at it today. Can you fill in the next line?

Pascal's Triangle

Draw this triangle on a piece of paper and see how far you can go.

20 August
Saint Stephen's Day in Hungary

Hungarians celebrate Saint Stephen's Day, and the foundation of the Hungarian state, with fireworks and all kinds of other entertainment. Every year a special Hungary birthday cake is baked. Eat some birthday cake to celebrate – and don't forget to sing, 'Happy birthday dear Hungary' before you eat it.

21 August
Usain Bolt's Birthday

Jamaican sprinter Usain Bolt was born on 21 August 1986. Practise being first out of the starting blocks.

22 AUGUST
Take a long journey

It's the holiday season, so if you're going on a long journey by car, plane or train today expand your geographical knowledge at the same time, by playing...

CITY ALPHABET

A player starts by naming a city. Then the next player has to name a city that starts with the last letter of the previous one. For example, Barcelona – Adelaide – Edinburgh – Hanover, etc. See if you can make it all the way around the world, or at least until the end of the alphabet.

23 AUGUST
Vulcanalia

Every 23 August the ancient Romans held the festival of Vulcanalia (Vulcan was the god of volcanoes and metal working). The Romans sacrificed animals and cooked them on bonfires. Instead, cut courgettes and peppers into 3-cm chunks and stick them on a skewer with some tomatoes and any meat you like. Brush them with olive oil and cook them on the barbecue for a few minutes on each side.

24 August

The eruption of Mount Vesuvius

Mount Vesuvius erupted on 24 August 79 AD and destroyed the town of Pompeii in Italy. So...

MAKE A VINEGAR VOLCANO

YOU NEED: a half-litre plastic bottle; vinegar; 2 tbsp baking powder; warm water; washing-up liquid; red food colouring.

1. Choose a site for your volcano – a place where making a mess won't matter.

2. Fill the bottle almost to the top with warm water. Add a squirt of washing-up liquid, a few drops of food colouring and the baking powder and give it all a shake.

3. Using a funnel, top up the bottle with vinegar and wait for your volcano to erupt.

25 August

Matthew Webb swims the channel

On 25 August 1875, Matthew Webb became the first person to swim the English Channel. Challenge yourself to swim the Channel in your local pool. If you can't manage it (the Channel is about 1,334 lengths of a 25 metre pool), why not see how many lengths you can do?

26 August
National Dog Day

It's the day to celebrate our canine friends, at least in the US. Take a dog for a walk today, and give him an extra doggy treat. If you don't have a dog and can't borrow one, be nice to another pet ... or, failing that, your little brother.

27 August
Giant Platypus Throwing

Go along to Nymboida in New South Wales, Australia, to take part in this annual event held at the end of August. Don't worry, no animals are harmed. The platypus involved is made of plastic. If you can't make it to New South Wales, find a plastic platypus and see how far you can throw it.

28 August
La Tomatina

La Tomatina is a festival, held on the last Wednesday of August every year in the town of Bunol, Spain. More than 150,000 over-ripe tomatoes are thrown by thousands of participants in a huge tomato fight. Chuck a tomato today.

29 August

Ancient Egyptian New Year

Today is the first day of the ancient Egyptian calendar.
Hold a New Year party, and get your friends to dress up as
ancient Egyptians (use a lot of heavy eye make-up), or ancient
Egyptian gods (see 15 August).

30 August

Mary Shelley's birthday

*Mary Wollstonecraft Shelley was born on 30 August 1797. She's most famous for writing **Frankenstein**. Curl up with a horror story today, but don't forget to leave every light in the house on.*

31 AUGUST

Independence Day in Trinidad and Tobago

Trinidad and Tobago is the birthplace of limbo. So, today is the perfect day to...

LEARN HOW TO LIMBO

YOU NEED: a limbo pole (this could be a broom handle); music with a strong beat

1. Rest the limbo pole on two chair backs (or other items of furniture).

2. Turn on the music.

3. Attempt to dance underneath the pole by bending backwards. Place your feet about shoulder width apart and put your arms out to the sides for balance. Bend your legs and your back gradually as you approach the pole. Don't start to straighten up until a count of three after the pole has passed your eyes.

4. If you are successful, lower the pole and then try to dance under it again.

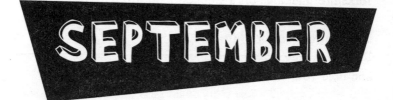

1 SEPTEMBER

Largs Viking Festival

Around 1 September every year, the Largs Viking Festival celebrates all things Viking.

MATCH THE VIKING NAMES

1) Eric   a) Hairy Breeches
2) Sigurd   b) Bluetooth
3) Ivar   c) Bloodaxe
4) Ragnar   d) Snake-in-the-eye
5) Harold   e) the Boneless

Answers: 1)c; 2)d; 3)e; 4)a; 5)b.

2 September

Black Pudding Throwing Championships

Every September, this unlikely competition is held at the Royal Oak pub in Ramsbottom, UK. Have a go at knocking a pile of Yorkshire puddings off a wooden platform with three throws of a black pudding. The tradition echoes the rivalry between Lancashire and Yorkshire and has been held for more than 150 years. Buy a black pudding and some Yorkshire puddings, and hold your own contest.

3 September

National Welsh Rarebit Day

Welsh rarebit – or cheese-on-toast – has its own national day in the US. Celebrate the day yourself and...

MAKE WELSH RAREBIT

YOU NEED: 50 ml milk; 225 g cheddar cheese, grated; 1 tsp mustard powder; 25 g unsalted butter; salt and pepper; 4 slices bread, toasted

1. Put the milk in a saucepan over a low heat.

2. Add the grated cheese and mustard powder. Stir the mixture until it's smooth and creamy.

3. Add the butter and keep stirring until melted.

4. Spoon the mixture over the toast and place it under a hot grill until it's golden brown.

4 SEPTEMBER

Fall of the Roman Empire

In 476 AD, the barbarian leader Odoacer, toppled the Roman Empire in the West, and kicked out the Emperor Romulus Augustus. Test your barbarian knowledge: here are six genuine barbarian tribes at the time of the Roman Empire, and two we've made up. Which two are false?

Franks   Picts   Vandals   Alans
Huns   Hooligans   Goths   Kevins

Answers: Hooligans and Kevins.

5 SEPTEMBER

Mark Ramprakash's birthday

The famous cricketer Mark Ramprakash was born today in 1969. If you don't have a huge cricket pitch and 21 friends who want to play cricket, you could...

PLAY FRENCH CRICKET

YOU NEED: at least six players; a tennis ball; a bat

1. Everyone stands in a circle. One person is chosen to bat first and he or she stands in the middle, facing the bowler.
2. The batter stands with his or her feet together and defends his or her legs below the knee with the bat. The other players take it in turns to bowl the ball at the batter's legs.

3. If the batter hits the ball, he or she is allowed to move his or her feet to face the next bowler. But if the batter misses, he or she has to keep his or her feet in the same position and can only turn his or her body to face the next bowler.

4. If one of the other players hits the batter's legs, or if one of them catches the ball after it has been hit, but before it has bounced, the batter is out.

5. Points are awarded for hitting the ball. The player with the most points is the winner.

6 SEPTEMBER

The Mayflower sets sail

On 6 September 1620, the Pilgrims set sail from Plymouth on their ship the **Mayflower** to settle in North America.

The Native Americans introduced European settlers to pumpkins, so that's why pumpkin pie is eaten at Thanksgiving – and today if you fancy it.

7 September
Virgen de la Salud Fiesta

Every September the town of Algemesi in Spain holds an annual festival, with processions, music and feasting. Its highlight is on 7 and 8 September when the muixeranga (acrobats) arrive. They perform human pyramids and amazing acrobatics. If you can't attend the festival, at least attempt some acrobatics of your own (though a human pyramid might be a bit advanced).

8 September
New Amsterdam becomes New York

Today in 1664, the Dutch handed over the American city of New Amsterdam to the British, who renamed the city New York. Can you identify which famous New York landmark this is?

Answer: The Statue of Liberty.

9 SEPTEMBER
Grandparents' Day

At least, it is in the US. But wherever you are, celebrate it anyway. Visit them if you can, or send them a card if you can't.

10 SEPTEMBER
Hotdog Day

... in the US. Wherever you are, treat yourself to a sausage snack, complete with tomato ketchup and fried onions.

11 SEPTEMBER
First Famous Five books published

On this day in 1942, Enid Blyton's first Famous Five book, **Five on a Treasure Island**, was published for the first time. So today is the perfect day to have a ginger beer and a delicious ice lolly and go on an adventure.

12 SEPTEMBER
Lascaux caves discovered

On 12 September 1940, the Lascaux cave system in France was discovered by four teenagers. The caves are famous for their Stone-Age paintings which are around 16,000 years old. Paint a mural today! Make sure you get permission first, then come up with a bold design for your bedroom. You can always paint over it if you can't live with it.

13 September
Roald Dahl's birthday

The writer Roald Dahl was born today in 1916. Revisit some of your favourite Roald Dahl stories – or, if you've never read them before, borrow some Dahl books from the library . Try **Charlie and the Chocolate Factory**, **James and the Giant Peach** or **The BFG**. Even better, find a small child to read them to.

14 September
Nutting Day

In days gone by, children were given the day off school on 14 September to gather hazelnuts. You could suggest it to your school – perhaps you could plant a nut tree in the school playground. If that fails, get out the nutcrackers and have a nutty feast instead.

15 September
Carlsbad Caverns Bat Festival

300,000 bats live in Carlsbad Caverns, New Mexico, USA. In the middle of September every year, Carlsbad Caverns National Park holds its annual bat festival. Go bat spotting, even if you're nowhere near New Mexico. Bats live in most parts of the world, in towns as well as the countryside. Look for them at dusk – they can often be spotted swooping for insects over rivers and lakes.

16 September
David Copperfield's birthday

The magician David Copperfield was born today in 1956. He's famous for elaborate illusions, such as making the Statue of Liberty disappear. Today is the perfect day to learn how to perform…

A SIMPLE MAGIC TRICK

YOU NEED: a pack of cards

1. Ask an audience member to shuffle the pack.
2. Say you're going to pull out the first, second and third cards from the pack, but actually pull out the second, third and fourth and fan them out. Keep the real first card level with the rest of the pack. Try to make sure this isn't obvious.
3. Holding the pack away from you, so you can't see the card faces, display the pack face up to the audience.
4. Ask the audience to choose one of the three fanned cards without telling you what the card is – either one, two or three.
5. With the pack face down, stack it together again. Take the number of cards the audience chose from the top and put them anywhere in the pack, as if you're losing them. The actual card that the audience chose should now be on the top of the pack.

6. Now say the magic words to make the chosen card 'magically' rise to the top of the pack. Turn it over with a flourish.

7. Take a bow.

17 SEPTEMBER

Honey Month

September is Honey Month in the US. Make yourself delicious honey yoghurt using plain Greek yoghurt, a spoonful of runny honey, and a sprinkle of crushed pistachio nuts.

18 SEPTEMBER

Feast day of Joseph of Copertino

Joseph of Copertino was an Italian saint renowned for his ability to levitate. Why not learn your own levitation trick? Marvel as you...

FEEL YOUR ARMS MYSTERIOUSLY LEVITATE

1. Stand in a doorway with your arms touching either side of the door frame.

2. Push your arms hard against the door frame for at least 30 seconds.

3. Walk away from the doorway and relax. Your arms will mysteriously rise upwards!

4. Try this trick on your friends.

19 September

International Talk Like a Pirate Day

Yes, really. Today is your chance to be very silly indeed, safe in the knowledge that many other people are doing the same thing all over the world.

PIRATE DICTIONARY

Avast	Stop
Ahoy	Hello
Booty	Treasure
Fair winds	Good luck
Galley	Kitchen
Hornswaggler	Cheat
Jolly Roger	Pirate flag
Landlubber	A non-pirate
Pieces of eight	Silver coins cut into eight pieces

| Shark bate | A lazy, useless landlubber |
| Shiver me timbers! | Gosh! (or similar expression of surprise) |

20 SEPTEMBER
Air Guitar World Championships

Around this date, Finland holds the annual Air Guitar World Championships to commemorate the great guitarist Jimi Hendrix, who died on 18 September 1970. If you can't compete in the contest, you have the perfect excuse to practise your air guitar at home.

21 SEPTEMBER

H G Wells's birthday

The writer H G Wells was born today in 1866. He is most famous for being a science fiction writer. His books include **The Time Machine** and **The War of the Worlds**. Come up with your own science fiction story. Here are some tips...

• Decide whether you want to set your story on an alien planet or on this one – perhaps far into the future.

• Base your story on real scientific discoveries, such as cloning or robots that can think for themselves. What might come from these discoveries in the future?

• If you want to include aliens, come up with some really original ones. Perhaps, somewhere in the universe, intelligent life evolved from plants instead of animals?

• If your story is set on a future planet Earth, what has changed? Perhaps cloning is out of control, or humans have become slaves to maniac plant life that has taken over the world. Anything is possible.

• Be sure to include some good battle scenes.

22 September
OneWebDay

Since 2006, OneWebDay has been celebrating the World Wide Web every 22 September. It's a good day to revisit your favourite websites, or maybe discover some new ones.

23 September (late September)
World Gurning Championships

If you're good at making faces, take part in the World Gurning Championships which are held on the third Saturday in September every year in Cumbria, UK. If you can't make it, have a gurning contest with your friends or family instead.

24 SEPTEMBER
Anniversary of Dr Seuss's Death

Theodor Seuss Geisel, better known as Dr Seuss, died today in 1991. Find a copy of **The Cat in the Hat**, or one of Dr Seuss's other brilliant books, and read it today.

25 SEPTEMBER
NATIONAL COMIC BOOK DAY

*THIS IS A NATIONAL DAY IN THE US, BUT WHEREVER YOU LIVE IT GIVES YOU A GOOD EXCUSE TO READ A COMIC. OR, CREATE YOUR OWN COMIC STRIP, INCLUDING AS MANY **BIFFS**, **POWS** AND **THWACKS** AS YOU CAN.*

26 SEPTEMBER
International Rabbit Day

Appreciate a rabbit today. If you own a rabbit – the third most popular pet – give him or her an extra carrot today. If you don't have your own pet bunny, why not go out rabbit spotting? Early in the morning or dusk are good times to look for our floppy-eared friends.

27 September
World Tourism Day

Plan your ideal holiday today – it could be a beach holiday, or an activity holiday like skiing, scuba diving or horse riding. You might want to go somewhere unusual – to the Arctic Circle to see the northern lights, or even into space. Maybe you won't get there any time soon, but start planning now for the holiday of a lifetime in the future.

28 September
Michaelmas Eve

An old superstition says that it's unlucky to eat blackberries after Michaelmas Day (which is tomorrow), so go blackberry picking today. You could make a blackberry and apple pie with your harvest.

29 September
Michaelmas Day

The old tradition of eating goose on Michaelmas Day was once just as popular as eating turkey at Christmas is today. Have a big feast with your family and friends, though a chicken might be easier to find than a goose.

30 SEPTEMBER

Lang Ca Ong

Fishermen in Ba Ria-Vung Tau Province in Vietnam celebrate this festival, dedicated to whales, around this time every year. Today is a good day to learn some amazing…

BLUE WHALE FACTS

• Blue whales are the largest animals ever to have lived on Earth — yes, including the dinosaurs. They can grow to over 30 metres long, and weigh 200 tonnes.

• A blue whale's tongue can weigh more than an elephant.

• Instead of teeth, blue whales have filters for sieving small, shrimp-like creatures called krill from great mouthfuls of seawater. They can eat nearly 4 tonnes of krill a day.

1 October
World Vegetarian Day
Celebrate with this delicious dish...

MAKE VEGGIE BURGERS

YOU NEED: 1 x 420 g tin of chickpeas, rinsed and drained; 120 g mixed nuts, chopped; 1 medium onion, chopped; 2 carrots, grated; 30 g tomato puree; 1 egg, beaten; dried breadcrumbs

1. Mash the chickpeas, then stir in the nuts, onions, carrots, tomato puree and egg. Mix well and add salt and pepper.

2. Divide the mixture into four equally sized burgers. Coat the outside of each one with breadcrumbs.

3. Put the burgers in the fridge for an hour or so.

4. Grill the burgers under a medium-hot grill for about four minutes on each side.

5. Eat the burgers in buns with tomato and lettuce.

2 OCTOBER

Old Man's Day in Braughing, Hertfordshire, UK

On 2 October in the late 1500s, Matthew Wall was in his coffin being taken to church when one of the coffin bearers slipped and jolted the coffin. Matthew woke up, much to his surprise and everyone else's, and went on to live for several more years. The event is remembered in Braughing, when children sweep the lane with brooms, the funeral bell tolls, and Matthew's grave is tended. You could use Old Man's Day as an excuse to be extra nice to your granddad.

3 OCTOBER

World Smile Day

World Smile Day falls on the first Friday in October each year. An artist called Harvey Ball created the smiley face in 1963. Later, he created World Smile Day, a day for everyone to do good deeds and smile.

4 OCTOBER

Woolly Worm Festival in Banner Elk, North Carolina, USA

The main attraction of the Woolly Worm Festival, held every October, is the wooly worm racing. Woolly worms are the hairy, stripy caterpillars of tiger moths. They can climb surprisingly quickly. For $5 you can race your own worm up a string. The owner of the winning worm wins a cash prize. Get your friends together and have a go at caterpillar racing today. Or, if you can't find any caterpillars, why not try worm racing?

5 OCTOBER

Round-the-world walk

On 5 October 1974, David Kunst completed the first ever round-the-world walk. Set off on your own long walk today.

6 October

Dessert Month

You might not have heard that October is Dessert Month in the US. Treat it as an excuse to make – or at least eat – your favourite pudding today.

7 October

World Zombie Day

Every year, on the second Sunday in October, people all over the world dress up as zombies. They shuffle about groaning, to raise money for charity. Get out the grey make-up and fake blood and do your bit.

8 October

Space Week

Space week runs from 4 October (the anniversary of the launch of the first man-made satellite, Sputnik 1) to 10 October (the anniversary of the signing of the Outer Space Treaty in 1967). So...

BUILD A SCALE MODEL OF THE SOLAR SYSTEM

YOU NEED: a space hopper (preferably yellow); 2 grains of rice; 2 peas; a tennis ball; 1 snooker ball; 2 golf balls; sand

To keep the distances to roughly the same scale as the size of the planets, you would need to place the space hopper (the Sun) 2.5 km away from the last golfball (Neptune). To avoid this, this method divides the distances by 100.

1. Use your space hopper to represent the Sun.

2. Put a grain of rice 23 cm away from the space hopper. This is Mercury.

3. Put a pea 43 cm from the spacehopper. This is Venus.

4. Put the other pea 60 cm from the space hopper. This is Earth.

5. Place the other grain of rice 91 cm from the space hopper. This is Mars.

6. Sprinkle some sand about a meter from the spacehopper. This is the asteroid belt.

7. Put the tennis ball 113 cm from the spacehopper. This is Jupiter.

8. Set your snooker ball 139 cm away from the space hopper. This is Saturn.

9. Put one of the golf balls 187 cm from the spacehopper. This is Uranus.

10. The other golf ball goes another 65 cm away, 252 cm from the spacehopper. This is the planet Neptune.

11. Stand back and marvel at our planet's place in the universe.

9 OCTOBER

Duck racing in Tubingen, Germany

Thousands of plastic bath ducks are raced in Tubingen, near Stuttgart, every October. To take part, you must register your duck an hour before the start of the race. Or you could hold your own duck race on a stream near you.

10 OCTOBER

On 10 October 1881, the scientist Charles Darwin published the book he considered to be his most important work – the catchily titled, **The Formation of Vegetable Mould Through the Action of Worms**. Darwin dug up his garden to count the worms. Darwin calculated that an average acre of garden contained 53,767 worms. Appreciate a worm today.

11 October
Celebrate autumn

Collect some autumn leaves today and have a go at a Japanese art form…

HAPA ZOME

YOU NEED: old cotton sheet; autumn leaves; chopping board; hammer

1. On top of a chopping board, lay the leaves on one half of the sheet and cover with the other half.

2. Bash it with a hammer.

3. Open up the sheet, remove what's left of the leaves, and admire your colourful leaf-patterned fabric.

4. Ask an adult to set your design using an iron.

12 October
Mop Fair, Stratford-upon-Avon, UK

Mop fairs, when servants, farm workers and craftspeople presented themselves for employment, used to be held all over England. Stratford-upon-Avon still holds its Mop Fair, but today it's a funfair! Go on the first morning of the fair, which is on or near 12 October, when children can go on the rides free of charge. If you can't get to Stratford, see if you can find a funfair near where you live.

13 OCTOBER
Anniversary of Claudius I's death

On this day in AD 54, the Roman Emperor Claudius I died, and Nero became Emperor of Rome. Try this simple quiz and find out how much you know about those crazy Roman rulers.

MATCH THE EMPEROR TO THE BONKERS DEED

1. Claudius

a. Smothered his dinner guests to death with rose petals.

2. Caligula

b. Passed a law allowing people to fart at the dinner table.

3. Nero

c. Removed the heads from the statues of gods and replaced them with his own.

4. Elegabalus

d. Killed his own mother.

Answers: 1)b; 2)c; 3)d; 4)a.

14 October
Turnip Day

The French republican calendar was used in France from 1793 until 1805, and used 12 months made up of three ten-day weeks. Our 14 October was the French republican calendar's Turnip Day. To celebrate, have a go at making this unusual snack...

MAKE TURNIP CHIPS

YOU NEED: turnip; vegetable oil; salt

1. Preheat the oven to 180°C. Cut the turnip into long, thin chips and brush them with oil.

2. Sprinkle some salt over them and place them on a baking tray.

3. Bake for about 20 minutes.

15 October
Grouch Day

Today is inspired by the Sesame Street character Oscar the Grouch. You are allowed to be as grumpy as you like today. As long as you make up for it by being extra cheerful tomorrow.

16 October
Oscar Wilde's birthday

Oscar Wilde was born today in 1859. He was a famous writer and is well known for having said some funny things. Contemplate some witty 'Wildean' remarks and see if you can use them today.

'Always forgive your enemies: nothing annoys them so much'

'He has no enemies but is intensely disliked by his friends'

'I can resist everything except temptation'

'Some cause happiness wherever they go; others whenever they go'

17 October
Wear Something Gaudy Day

At least, it is the US – but you can wear something gaudy wherever you are.

18 OCTOBER

Alaska Day

Alaska celebrates the day it became part of the US today...

MAKE BAKED ALASKA

YOU NEED: a ready-made flan case; raspberry jam; 650 ml tub of vanilla ice cream; 4 egg whites; 225 g caster sugar

1. Spread the flan case with raspberry jam and put the ice cream on top. Leave it in the freezer for at least an hour.

2. Preheat the oven to 230°C/ gas mark 8.

3. Make a meringue by whisking the egg whites until they form stiff peaks and don't slide around in the bowl. Whisk in the sugar a little at a time.

4. Take the flan and ice cream out of the freezer and spread the meringue all over it.

5. Put it in the oven for 3 or 4 minutes, until the outside has browned slightly.

6. Eat straight away, for a hot-and-cold-at-the-same-time experience.

19 October

Heikki Kovalainen's birthday

Today is the birthday of Finnish racing driver Heikki Kovalainen, born in 1981. Find a carting track near you and pretend you are driving in a Grand Prix.

20 October

The opening of the Sydney Opera House

On this day in 1973, the Sydney Opera House was opened. According to some people, it's one of the Modern Wonders of the World, alongside buildings such as Angkor Wat in Cambodia, the Taj Mahal in India, Machu Picchu in Peru, The Great Wall of China, and the Coloseum in Rome. Find out about the Seven Wonders of the Ancient World today.

THE SEVEN WONDERS OF THE ANCIENT WORLD

The Lighthouse at Alexandria
The Colossus of Rhodes
The Statue of Zeus at Olympia
The Mausoleum at Halicarnassus
The Great Pyramid at Giza
The Hanging Gardens of Babylon
The Temple of Artemis at Ephesus

21 October

Apple Day

Apple Day is celebrated in the UK, every 21 October. One of the day's events is a competition to make the longest single piece of apple peel – why not have a go? Or try apple-bobbing with some friends: fill a washing-up bowl with water and float some apples in it – players have to try and take an apple out of the water using only their teeth.

22 October

The first parachute jump

On 22 October 1797, the first ever parachute jump was made by Andre Jacques Garnerin. You have to be aged 16 or over to make a parachute jump yourself, but you could make a mini-parachute...

MAKE A TOY PARACHUTE

YOU NEED: a piece of cotton fabric roughly 30 cm x 30 cm; four 40-cm pieces of string; a toy soldier

1. Tie a knot in each corner of the fabric.
2. Tie each piece of string to the fabric just above the knots.
3. Gather the loose ends of the string and tie them to the toy.
4. Spread out the parachute and drop it from a height. Experiment with toys of different weights.

23 October
Mole Day

A mole is a unit of amount of substance, as you might already know if you are interested in chemistry. The Avogadro constant is the number of atoms or molecules in one mole, and is approximately 6.02×10^{23}. Mole Day is celebrated between 6.02 in the morning and 6.02 in the evening, because if you write the date and time in the American style, it's 6:02 10/23. So today's the day to have a party in your chemistry lesson.

24 October
Play conkers

It's autumn, so it's compulsory to have at least one game of conkers. Gather some horse chestnuts, make a hole through the middle of each one and thread through a long piece of string. Find a friend with a conker and you're ready to play.

Wrap some of the string around your hand and dangle your conker for your friend to whack with his or her own conker. The winner is the first player to completely destroy the other's conker.

25 OCTOBER
Picasso's birthday

The artist Pablo Picasso was born on 25 October 1881. You might not be able to create a priceless masterpiece, but almost anyone can draw a doodle...

ANALYSE YOUR DOODLES

Is it true that those little pictures you doodle during maths lessons really say something significant about you? Well, probably not. But, just for fun, here are what some common doodles are supposed to mean...

- Boxes or geometric shapes: a sign of an ordered mind. You like to plan and organize.

- Swirls, non-geometric shapes: show a lack of concentration.

- Hearts: you are in love (obviously). Or, if you're not, maybe you would like to be.

- Sun, moon, stars: show that you are optimistic.

- Flowers: a sign that you are friendly and sensitive to others.

- Arrows or ladders: a sign that you are ambitious.

26 October (end of October)
Coffin Racing

Visit Manitou Springs in Colorado in the US, for this annual unusual race. competitors zoom down the main street in coffins on wheels as part of the Emma Crawford Festival, held every year around this time. The coffin racing commemorates Emma Crawford's unfortunate end: she was buried on the nearby Red Mountain in the nineteenth century, but many years later the ground eroded and the coffin slid down the mountain. If you're not in Colorado today, go sledging, skate-boarding or roller-skating instead.

27 October
National Tell a Story Day

Today's the day to tell someone a story – it's a national day in the UK. Wherever you are, find a small child and read them a story. Or, even better, tell them one you've made up yourself.

28 October
Bill Gates's birthday

Computing pioneer Bill Gates was born on this day in 1955. He's one of the richest people on Earth. Try to start your own multi-billion-pound fortune today. Ask your parents if there's anything you can do for them for financial reward. Well, it's a start ...

29 October (last Thursday in October)
Punkie Night

Punkie Night is still celebrated in Somerset, England, where children roam the streets chanting:

It's Punkie Night tonight,
It's Punkie Night tonight,
Give us a candle, give us a light,
It's Punkie Night tonight.

A punkie is a jack-o-lantern, traditionally made from a turnip, but pumpkins are much easier to carve. Here are some ideas for your design:

30 October
Mischief Night

In some parts of England, Scotland, Ireland, Canada and the US, the tradition is for children to play pranks on Mischief Night. Choose from smearing doorknobs with treacle, knocking on doors and running away, and other naughtiness.

31 OCTOBER
Halloween

If you're going to a party today, try these simple yet effective costumes:

VAMPIRE VICTIM – wear pyjamas or a nightie. Make an eye-catching fake vampire wound on your neck by drawing on the two distinctive bite marks with a red marker pen, and drizzling on fake blood made from syrup and red food colouring. Attach a rubber bat to your shoulder.

HORROR-MOVIE VICTIM – wear ordinary clothes, with the addition of a joke 'axe-in-the-head', available from joke shops. Make some fake blood from syrup and red food colouring and drip this gruesomely from your head wound.

GHOST – wear old-fashioned clothes in grey, white or black, use white or grey make-up for any skin that's going to show, and dust your clothes and your hair with lots of flour. Spooky!

MACBETH'S WITCHES – get together with two friends. You don't have to wear pointy hats – you could be glamorous witches with lots of make-up and long black wigs. You'll need a cauldron and some gruesome ingredients to put into it. If you can't find eye of newt and wing of bat, make do with some rubber spiders, snakes and toads. Practise cackling.

NOVEMBER

1 NOVEMBER
Day of the Dead in Mexico

People in Mexico celebrate the lives of friends and family members who have died in a two-day festival starting today. Graves are decorated, stories about dead friends are told, and everyone has a feast – it's a happy occasion, despite all the skeletons, skulls, coffins and gravestones used as decoration. Try making this traditional Day of the Dead sweet...

MAKE SUGAR SKULLS

YOU NEED: 200 g granulated sugar; 1 tsp dried egg-white powder; water; ready-made icing; food colouring

1. Mix together the sugar and egg-white powder.
2. Sprinkle on a tablespoon of water and mix until the sugar mixture is the texture of damp sand.
3. Shape the sugar into skull shapes on a baking sheet.
4. Leave the skulls to dry for 24 hours, or until they've hardened.
5. Decorate with icing mixed with dark food colouring.

2 NOVEMBER
All Souls' Day

The old tradition on All Soul's Day used to be for poorer people to call on their wealthier neighbours and offer to pray for the dead relatives in return for money or soul cakes. Try making soul cakes today – use the recipe for hot cross buns on 8 April but leave off the cross.

3 November
Sandwich Day

The sandwich is supposed to be named after John Montagu who was the Fourth Earl of Sandwich. He was born on 3 November 1718, and that's why today is Sandwich Day. Make yourself your favourite sandwich today. Try avocado, peanut butter, lettuce and tomato, or mozzarella, tomato and basil. Or why not try a sweet sandwich – a banana and chocolate one, perhaps?

4 November
Ringing Night

In some parts of England on the night before Guy Fawkes Night, there's a bell-ringing tradition. In Devon, bells are rung and children are given biscuits to eat. So if you can't ring a church bell or go to watch some bell ringers, you should at least have a biscuit to celebrate.

5 November
Guy Fawkes' Night

Guy Fawkes, part of a failed conspiracy to blow up the Houses of Parliament in 1605, is remembered in Britain on 5 November with fireworks and bonfires. To keep alive the tradition of burning a Guy on your bonfire, you need to...

MAKE A LIFE-LIKE GUY

YOU NEED: newspaper; old clothes (at least a pair of trousers and a sweatshirt); string; a pair of tights to make the head; a mask; wool for hair (optional)

1. Rip the newspaper into separate pages and roll each sheet up into a ball.

2. Tie up the bottom of each leg of the pair of trousers with string. Do the same with the arms on the sweatshirt.

3. Stuff the arms of the sweatshirt with the balls of newspaper.

4. Stuff the trousers with newspaper, stuffing the paper right down into the bottoms of the legs and working your way up to the waist.

5. When you're getting close to the waist of the trousers, stuff the sweatshirt inside the waistband and continue stuffing. You might need to secure it with a piece of string.

6. When you have your legs and body, begin on the head. Cut a leg off an old pair of tights and stuff it with balls of newspaper until it is roughly head-shaped. Tie up the bottom with string and attach it to the body.

7. Add the mask to the front of the head for a face. You could attach pieces of wool to the back of the mask for hair.

8. Sit your Guy at a street corner and shout 'Penny for the Guy!' at passers-by.

6 NOVEMBER
Chuck a pumpkin

Pumpkin chucking, or 'punkin chunkin', competitions are held all over the world, but especially in the US. The World Championships are held in Delaware on the first weekend after Halloween. Competitors use machines, such as catapults, trebuchets and air cannons, to try and hurl their pumpkins further than anyone else. Hold your own contest today. If you don't have a trebuchet handy, throw your pumpkin as far as you can using your own muscle power.

7 NOVEMBER (early November)
Giant Omelette Celebration in Abbeville, USA

Head for Abbeville in Louisiana if you're a fan of omelettes. For their annual festival they create a giant one, made with 5,000 eggs. Or you could make a big omelette for your family, though you probably won't need that many eggs!

8 NOVEMBER
Mundus patet

8 November was one of three days in the ancient Roman calendar when the doorway to the Underworld (the world of the dead, represented by a real pit, covered by a stone) was opened. Have another Halloween party – this time dressed as an ancient Roman.

9 November

Inventors' Day

Today is Inventors' Day in Europe because it is Hedy Lamarr's birthday – she was an Austrian-born US scientist, who was also a famous Hollywood actress. Spend the day inventing: all sorts of things are crying out to be invented – time-travel, a way of controlling the weather, teleportation … make a start today.

10 November

In the US, November is National Peanut Lovers' Month. So use today to learn how to…

MAKE PEANUT BUTTER

YOU NEED: 500 g peanuts; 2 tbsp groundnut oil; salt to taste

1. If your peanuts are not already roasted, roast them on a baking tray in a cool oven for 10–15 minutes. Rub off their skins with a tea towel

2. Grind the nuts using a blender. How long you grind them depends on how crunchy you want your peanut butter to be.

3. Add the oil until you get the consistency you want. Add salt to taste.

11 November

Go for an autumn walk in the woods today. Gather some autumn leaves and have a go at hapa zome when you get back (see 11 October).

12 November

Look out for a monster

On 12 November 1933, the first photos supposedly of the Loch Ness Monster were taken. Over the years there have been other photographs, and various sightings, but the monster's existence has never been proved. Keep your eyes peeled for a monster today, and keep your camera handy.

13 November

World Kindness Day

Share your packed lunch, help an old lady with her shopping, let someone on the bus in front of you … do something kind today. It'll prepare you for the International Day for Tolerance in a few days' time.

14 November (mid-November)

Gioco dell'Oca in Mirano, Italy

The Italian game Gioco dell'Oca ('Goose Game') is a bit like snakes and ladders – but with geese. The town of Mirano, holds a giant version, using people as counters, between the town's six different districts. Go along and watch players climbing ladders and hurdling geese, or play your own game of snakes and ladders instead.

15 NOVEMBER
The first modern Olympics

On 15 November 1859, the first modern international revival of the ancient Greek Olympic games was held in Athens, Greece. Try an Olympic sport today – there are lots to choose from, including polo, badminton, judo, archery, synchronized swimming, canoeing and mountain biking.

16 NOVEMBER
International Day for Tolerance

No matter how much something – or someone – annoys you today, remember that today is the International Day for Tolerance and bite your tongue. If you can last the whole day being tolerant, that is seriously impressive. Can you do it tomorrow, too? How many days do you think you can manage before you crack?

17 NOVEMBER
August Ferdinand Mobius' birthday

Today is the birthday of the German mathematician and astronomer August Ferdinand Mobius, born in 1790. He's probably most famous for the Mobius strip...

MAKE A MOBIUS STRIP

1. Cut a long, thin rectangle of paper (2 cm x 10 cm).
2. Give it a half twist.
3. Tape the ends together.

You now have a loop of paper with only one surface and one edge. To prove it, draw a line along the length. How many sides does it have? Now take a pair of scissors and cut along the line you drew along the length, and see what happens.

18 NOVEMBER (mid-November)
Biggest Liar in the World Contest

Every November, the Bridge Inn at Santon Bridge in Cumbria, UK, holds a competition to find the greatest teller of tall tales. If you want to take part, you get five minutes to tell a huge porky while keeping a straight face. If you can't make it to Cumbria, have a go at home. Five minutes is longer than you think.

19 November

World Toilet Day

Yes, really. Appreciate your toilet today — and try this
toilet quiz...

1. In a row of public toilets, which cubicle
is likely to be the least used?
a) The last in the row
b) The middle toilet
c) The first in the row

2. True or false? Thomas Crapper invented
the flushing toilet.

3. How many times does the average person
visit the toilet in a year?
a) 5,000 times a year
b) 2,500 times a year
c) 1,000 times a year

4. True or false? Ancient Romans had public
toilets but no separate cubicles.

Answers: 1)c; 2)false; 3)b; 4)true.

20 November
The invention of traffic lights

Traffic lights were invented on 20 November 1923. To celebrate, make traffic light treats for your friends: use oblong biscuits or crackers, spread them with peanut butter or chocolate spread, and put red, yellow and green sweets on them to make traffic lights.

21 November
World Hello Day

Hello Day has been celebrated since 1972. You can join in by saying 'hello' to ten different people today.

22 November
Anniversary of Blackbeard's death

Today in 1718, the famous pirate Blackbeard was killed in battle. Make a treasure hunt for younger brothers or sisters, or even for your friends.

MAKE A PIRATE TREASURE HUNT

Hide slips of paper, with clues written on them, around your house or garden – the final clue should lead to a treasure map, with 'X' marking the spot. The treasure could be sweets or other small treats. Use some pirate-themed stickers to help your treasure hunters find the clues. Here are a few ideas:

- Yarr! Look in the galley for a yellow parrot. (Put a parrot sticker on a kitchen drawer . . . put the next clue inside the drawer.)

- Avast there! Time for another clue? (Put the next clue behind a clock.)

- Take five paces. The next clue's to be found at the sign of the crossbones. (Use another sticker for this one – place the next clue five paces in any direction from the last one.)

- Include five or six clues. For the last one, draw a map of the room, marking where you've hidden the treasure with an 'X'.

23 NOVEMBER
St Clements Day

An old English custom was for children to visit people's houses, expecting treats or money in return. This tradition was known as 'clementing'. If you want to try it, here's the rhyme you should recite at people's doors:

Clementing, clementing, once a year,
Apples and pears are very good cheer.
If you have no apples, money will do,
Money will do, money will do.

24 NOVEMBER
Evolution Day

Today is the anniversary of the first publication of Charles Darwin's book **The Origin of Species**, published in 1859. Spend the day finding out about evolution, marvelling at the mysterious beginnings of life on our planet, which started off as a few microscopic organisms, stayed that way for billions of years, then gradually evolved into all the amazing creatures on Earth today.

25 NOVEMBER
Thanksgiving

Around this time of year (on the fourth Thursday of November) it's Thanksgiving in the US, remembering the Pilgrims' first winter in America. It's traditionally celebrated with a turkey dinner, but you could make some turkey-shaped gingerbread instead (see page 103 for a recipe).

26 NOVEMBER (last Sunday in November)
Stir-up Sunday

Stir-up Sunday is the traditional day for starting to make your Christmas pudding. If it seems a little early to be doing that, here's a list of ingredients – you can see you might have to spend some time getting them all together.

YOU NEED: suet; **flour; mixed spice;** nutmeg; **cinnamon;** brown sugar; **sultanas;** raisins; **currants;** candied peel; **almonds;** apples; **oranges;** lemons; **eggs**

Make a start today.

27 NOVEMBER
Anders Celsius's birthday

Anders Celsius, the Swedish astronomer and inventor of the centigrade temperature scale, was born today in 1701. To celebrate his birthday...

MAKE YOUR OWN THERMOMETER

This is a very simple thermometer, but it really works.

YOU NEED: a clear plastic bottle; a clear drinking straw; some sticky tack or play dough; water; food colouring

1. Take the lid off the bottle and make a small hole in it, just big enough to push the straw through.

2. Push the straw through the lid so that at least 6 cm are sticking out of the top. Seal the area around the straw with sticky tack – it needs to be completely air tight.

3. Fill the bottle about three quarters full with water and add a few drops of food colouring. Screw the lid back on to the bottle tightly.

4. Mark the position of the water line on the straw. Now stand your bottle somewhere much hotter or colder.

5. If your thermometer has been standing somewhere hot, the water line should have risen above the the line you marked on the straw. If it's been somewhere cold, it should have gone down.

If your thermometer hasn't worked, it's probably because it isn't airtight – add some more sticky tack to the joins around the straw and the lid.

28 NOVEMBER
Red Planet Day

Red Planet Day commemorates the launch of the spacecraft Mariner 4, on a mission to the red planet, Mars today in 1964. Find out some...

MARTIAN FACTS

Mars is named after the Roman god of war, and is the closest planet to Earth.

The planet's red colour is caused by the presence of the chemical compound iron oxide on its surface.

Until Mariner 4, people thought there might be seas, continents and perhaps life on the planet. Water has been found, but only as ice.

Mars has the highest mountain in our solar system: Olympus Mons is 27 km high.

Since Mariner 4 there have been other missions to Mars, including unmanned landings.

29 November
Fiesta de Las Tablas in Tenerife
On the eve of Saint Andrew's Day, local winemakers in the town of Icod de los Vinos in Tenerife hold a festival. Go along and watch local young men take part in the festival's old tradition of sliding down the town's sloped streets on wooden boards greased with tar. Or you could ride your skateboard or go sledging instead – it's probably best to leave out the tar.

30 November
Saint Andrew's Day
Saint Andrew is Scotland's patron saint (he is also the patron saint of Russia, Greece and Romania) and his feast day is Scotland's national day. So fly a Saltire (Scotland's national flag) today, or wear a thistle (the national flower).

1 December

National Samba Day in Brazil

At the beginning of December every year, Brazil celebrates its national dance. In the capital city, Rio de Janeiro, musicians play on trains heading to the suburbs, and perform a free concert.

Even if you can't make it to the suburbs of Rio, use today to learn how to dance the samba. Try looking on www.learntodance.com for instructions.

PHEEP!

2 DECEMBER
Georges Seurat's birthday

The artist Georges Seurat was born today in 1859. He's famous for a technique called pointillism – using dots of colour next to one another to make different colours, instead of mixing them. Make your own pointillist picture today – sketch your picture with a pencil, then use cotton buds to apply dots of coloured paint.

3 DECEMBER
Tree Dressing Day

The first full weekend of December is the time to celebrate trees. Visit an arboretum today if you can. Or make some decorations to hang on your Christmas tree later in the month.

1. Take a balloon and blow it up so it fits in the palm of your hand.

2. Cover it in three coats of papier mâché, letting it dry between each coat.

3. When it's dry, pop the balloon with a pin and take it out.

4. Paint the bauble and glue beads and glitter to it.

5. Bend a piece of wire into a loop and push it into the hole in the bauble to hang it from.

4 December

The discovery of the MARIE CELESTE

On 4 December 1872, the ship the Marie Celeste was spotted in the Atlantic Ocean, without a soul on board. Nobody knows what became of her crew. Write your own mystery story today. You could find out if there have been any mysterious events in your area, or imagine what happened on board the Marie Celeste.

5 December

Saint Nicholas's Eve

This is the day everyone exchanges their Christmas presents in Holland, instead of on Christmas Day, Christmas Eve, or 6 January as in lots of other countries. If you're saving your present-giving until later, today might be a good day to make some inexpensive Christmas presents...

CREATE A PERSONALIZED CHRISTMAS BOX: decorate an old shoe box with Christmas wrapping paper and tinsel and fill it with some of your friend or relative's favourite things – sweets, bubble bath or stickers, for example.

MAKE A SIMPLE PHOTO FRAME: use thin card covered in papier mâché, and include a photo of yourself with the person you are giving the gift to.

6 DECEMBER (around this date)
Great Christmas Pudding Race

In Covent Garden in London, UK, teams race one another over an obstacle course, balancing a Christmas pudding on a tray. If you can't go along and watch, hold your own pudding race with your mates.

7 DECEMBER
The eve of the feast day of The Virgin of the Immaculate Conception

In Guatemala, people have a major clean-up today. Homes are cleaned and cleared out and all the rubbish is put in a heap in the street. In the evening, the piles of rubbish are set on fire. People believe that evil is burned along with the rubbish. Have a grand clear out today but instead of burning all your unwanted bits and pieces, recycle them.

8 DECEMBER
National Chocolate Brownie Day
Help celebrate this American national day in the only way possible.

9 DECEMBER
Anna's Day
In Finland and Sweden, today is Anna's Day – a special day to honour everyone called Anna. If you know an Anna, do something nice for her. If you're called Anna, even better! Let everyone know about your special day.

10 DECEMBER
Ada Lovelace's birthday
Ada Lovelace, English countess and the first ever computer programmer, was born on 10 December 1815. Learn a new computer program, or play a new game, in her honour.

11 DECEMBER
Viswanathan Anand's birthday
Chess Grandmaster and World Chess Champion, Viswanathan Anand, was born on 11 December 1969. Set up your own chess tournament today – or learn how to play if you don't already know how to.

12 December
The first transatlantic radio message transmitted

On this day in 1901, the inventor Guglielmo Marconi changed international communications forever when he received a message which had beent transmitted in England on his receiver in Canada. Do your bit for international communications today – email a friend in another country.

13 December
Feast of Saint Lucia

In Sweden, the eldest daughter in the family performs an old custom to celebrate the feast of Saint Lucia. If you want to have a go, here's how...

- **Get up at dawn.**
- **Wear a white gown with a red sash, and a wreath on your head with four candles burning on it.**
- **Serve breakfast while singing a special song.**

14 December
Monkey Day

Monkey Day is celebrated every year on this date, mainly by people who like to dress up in monkey costumes (see also Gorilla Suit Day on page 28). Dress up as a monkey today.

15 December

Ten days until Christmas

Why not use today to make your own Christmas decorations from salt dough?

SALT-DOUGH DECORATIONS

YOU NEED: 2 quantities of flour (these could be cups, or any amount you like – the important thing is to get the ratio of 2:1:1); 1 quantity of salt; 1 quantity of water; shaped biscuit cutters; greaseproof paper

1. Mix together the flour and salt in a bowl. Gradually add the water, and stir to make a soft dough.

2. Leave the dough for 20 minutes or so before you start using it.

3. Roll out the dough to about a $\frac{1}{2}$ cm thick. Cut out shapes with biscuit cutters. If you want to hang up the decorations, make a hole in the top of them with a chopstick or a knitting needle.

4. Put the shapes on greaseproof paper on a baking sheet, and put them in a cool oven (100°C / gas mark $\frac{1}{4}$) for about four hours.

5. Turn off the oven and leave your dough shapes to cool down inside. Then decorate them with paints, glue, glitter or whatever you like.

16 December

Chocolate-covered Anything Day

This is another American national day that gives us all an excuse to eat sweets. Have you tried chocolate-covered strawberries, marshmallows, breadsticks, sausages...?

17 December

Saturnalia

17 December was the start of the ancient Roman festival of Saturnalia. This festival included lots of eating, drinking, partying, gift-giving and decorating homes with evergreen plants – rather like our own Christmas festival. People swapped roles as part of the festival – masters became slaves and teachers became pupils. Why not suggest a similar swap today?

18 December

The film director Steven Spielberg (born in 1946) and the film star Brad Pitt (born in 1964) share a birthday on 18 December. Go to the movies today, or watch your favourite DVD at home.

19 December

Liberation Day in Goa

Goa became independent from Portugal in on 19 December 1961. Help celebrate by making this delicious Goan sweet, especially popular at Christmas time.

Make Goan Milk Cream

YOU NEED: 1 litre milk; 450 g caster sugar; 100 g cashew nuts, ground; 1 tbsp butter; small moulds (such as a shaped ice-cube tray)

1. In a saucepan, boil the milk slowly over a low heat until it's reduced by about half.

2. Add the sugar, stirring all the time until the sugar dissolves and the mixture thickens.

3. Add the cashew nuts and keep stirring to make sure the mixture doesn't stick to the pan.

4. When the mixture starts to bubble at the sides of the pan, remove it from the heat and leave it to cool.

5. Butter the moulds and spoon in the cooled mixture.

6. Leave the milk creams to set overnight in the moulds, then turn them out.

20 December
Go Carolling Day
Keep up an old tradition and go carol singing today (it's national Go Carolling Day in the US). You could get a group of friends together to form a choir. Make sure everyone knows all the words, and try out some harmonies.

21 December
Winter solstice
Today, (or tomorrow in the northern hemisphere) is the shortest day and longest night of the year. Celebrate as they did in ancient times and bring a yule log into your home – it can be either oak or pine, and you should carve a picture of the Sun on it. As it burns in your fireplace, think of the coming spring. Save a piece of it to protect your home in the coming year and use it to light next year's yule log. If you don't have a fireplace for your ancient ritual, have a slice of chocolate yule log instead.

22 December (winter months)

Wassailling

In the past, people would knock on doors, singing songs and asking for a 'wassail' in return – this could be something to eat or drink. It's a good idea to have a hot winter drink ready in case any wassailers stop by.

MAKE SPICED WINTER PUNCH

These quantities are just a rough guide – you can vary them, and a 'cup' can be whatever size you like.

YOU NEED: 8 cups apple juice; 1 cup soft brown sugar; 10 cloves; 3 cinnamon sticks; 4 cups orange juice; 2 cups pineapple juice; 1 orange, sliced

1. In a saucepan, mix together the apple juice, sugar, cinnamon and cloves and bring it slowly to the boil.

2. Lower the heat and simmer for a few minutes.

3. Add the orange juice and pineapple juice and heat through without boiling.

4. Pour into cups and serve with slices of orange.

23 DECEMBER
The Night of the Radishes

This special event takes place in Oaxaca City, Mexico, every 23 December. Crowds gather for a display of elaborate sculptures carved from huge radishes – the creator of the best one gets his or her picture in the morning paper. Try carving your own radish today.

24 DECEMBER
Christmas Eve

In Denmark (and lots of other countries) Christmas Eve is the focus for Christmas celebrations. Follow the diagrams below to make a traditional Danish decoration today.

MAKE WOVEN CHRISTMAS HEARTS

YOU NEED: two different colours of wrapping paper; scissors; glue stick

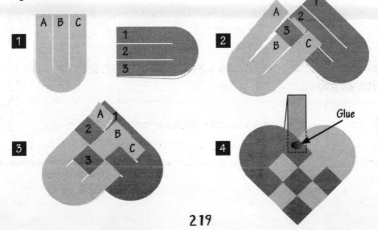

25 DECEMBER

Christmas Day

Set your relatives this international Christmas quiz...

1. In Greece, underground goblins called kallikantzaroi are supposed to roam the earth between 25 December and 6 January. What keeps them at bay?
a) burning Christmas pudding
b) burning holly leaves
c) burning old shoes

2. True or false? In Holland, Father Christmas rides a white horse.

3. In which country does an old woman known as Baboushka give out Christmas presents?

4. What's unusual about the Japanese Christmas gift-giver?
a) he has two heads
b) he has eyes in the back of his head
c) he balances the gifts in a pile on his head

5. Who gives out the Christmas presents in Syria?
a) a reindeer
b) a donkey
c) a camel

6. 'Feliz Navidad' means 'Happy Christmas' in which language?

Answers: 1)c; 2) True; 3)Russia; 4)b; 5)c; 6)Spanish.

26 December

Boxing Day

If you find yourself sitting at the dinner table with a group of relatives over the holiday season, feeling too full to move, try this game...

20 Christmas questions

Everyone takes it in turns to think of a character or an animal related to Christmas or winter. Here are some suggestions: Ebeneezer Scrooge; a turkey; a robin; Frosty the Snowman; the Grinch; Rudolph; a polar bear; a partridge in a pear tree. The other players have to guess what it is, using a maximum of 20 questions. The questions can only be answered 'yes', 'no' or 'I don't know'.

27 December

National Fruitcake Day

If you're not already full of Christmas cake, have a piece of fruitcake today to celebrate this American national day.

28 December

Holy Innocents' Day

Today is a good day to do nothing at all, because it's supposed to be the unluckiest day of the year (unless you're a Saxon, in which case it's 2 January).

221

29 December
Pepper Pot Day

On 29 December 1777, during the American Revolutionary War, legend has it that George Washington asked his army chef to come up with a hearty soup for his troops. The chef found some peppercorns, tripe (stomach lining) and a few scraps of meat, and produced Pepper Pot Soup, which became known as 'the soup that won the war'. Make a peppery winter soup today – but perhaps leave out the tripe.

30 December
We're not alone

On 30 December 1924, astronomer Edwin Hubble announced the existence of other galaxies. The Hubble telescope is named after him – look up some of the amazing pictures it has taken of distant galaxies at hubblesite.org/gallery.

31 December
New Year's Eve

In Scotland, New Year's Eve (or Hogmanay) is celebrated with more enthusiasm than almost anywhere else in the world.

Celebrate like a Scot

• Clean your home from top to bottom. Hang rowan branches over the front door.

• Have a big party and invite lots of friends. Kiss everyone to wish them a happy new year.

• At midnight, link arms and sing 'Auld Lang Syne'. Lots of people get the words wrong, so here they are:

AULD LANG SYNE

Should auld acquaintance be forgot,
And never brought to mind?

Should auld acquaintance be forgot,
And auld lang syne.

For auld lang syne, my dear,
For auld lang syne.

We'll tak a cup o' kindness yet,
For auld lang syne.

• Don't forget to make your New Year's resolutions.